D1259735

About the Book

All of us know that without adequate supplies of clean, fresh water, we cannot exist. Yet few of us have ever considered the nature of water and the problems man has created for himself in using this indispensable natural resource.

In this thought-provoking book, Dr. L. A. Heindl outlines basic principles for the sound management of water and cites numerous specific examples of the difficulties—and sometimes catastrophes—which can result when these principles are abandoned or ignored.

His account tells, in part, of the relationship of water use and development and the dangerous pollution of America's rivers and Great Lakes; the recent drought in New York State; the ecological problems of the Everglades; the serious dilemmas arising from our wish to irrigate larger and larger areas of arid land; and our need to develop more water for day-to-day use, while at the same time preserving large areas of wilderness for wildlife and our own recreation.

Each of these vital questions is dealt with so discerningly that young readers cannot fail to grasp the interlocking problems involved in the management of water and the imperative need for their wise solution.

THE WATER

COWARD-McCANN, INC.   New York, N. Y.

WE LIVE BY

How to Manage It Wisely

BY L. A. HEINDL

Consultant: Matthew Brennan
UNESCO International Director
Venezuelan Conservation Curriculum Project
Center for Environmental Studies
Simon Bolivar University, Caracas, Venezuela

PHOTO CREDITS

Arizona State Museum, page 22
Department of Economic Development, St. Paul, Minnesota, page 101
Egyptian Tourist Administration, page 11
Stuart Finley, pages 79, 86, 87
Michigan Water Development Services, page 112
Ontario Department of Lands and Forests, page 111
Spanish National Tourist Office, page 29
Tennessee Valley Authority, page 42
United Nations, page 17
U.S. Army Corps of Engineers, pages 80, 82, 83, 111
U.S. Department of the Interior: Bureau of Reclamation, pages 6, 11, 12. 21, 22, 31, 34, 37, 51, 52, 69, 71, 74, 94, 101, 109; Geological Survey, pages 13, 20, 32, 38, 39, 76, 97, 106, 115, 117, 120; National Park Service, title page, pages 47, 48, 55, 61, 91, 95, 98, 126; Office of Saline Water, page 41
Wide World Photos, Inc., pages 64, 65
Diagrams, Adolph Brotman

CONTENTS

1

That's All There Is

Man has always known that he must have water to live. That knowledge was part of his heritage as he evolved to become *homo sapiens.* Later he learned how to use water to support permanent settlements and complex societies. Now, in this country and all over the world, in this day of rapid, sophisticated electronic and atomic advancement, he is learning that he is more dependent on water than ever before. He is learning that he will have to work as never before, spend money as never before, to provide himself with the water he wants, where he wants it, and fit to use as he wants to use it.

Not too long ago, when most of this nation's people lived along the east coast and in the well-watered region east of the Mississippi River, it was easy to believe that there was enough water for everyone for all time. But this was only a local and temporary situation. Although there is just as much water as ever before, there, too, water has become a problem.

Or rather *people* have become a problem. As more and more people move into a region or are born into it, the existing supplies must be made to stretch to satisfy ever-growing needs. Today the world's population is increasing faster than ever before. Not only that, each individual is striving to improve his standard of living, and thus more and more water is needed for human use and to provide the things and services we need. In the United States, for example, the use of water has increased about 15 percent every five years since 1950. For the same period, the population has increased at less than 3 percent for the same intervals.

As population increases and standards of living rise, so does pollution. And every added bit of pollution requires more water—more clean water—to dilute it and carry it away. In fact, the activities necessary to supply, use, and purify water increase in complexity as the demand for water rises.

Also, as population increases and standards of living rise, all kinds of problems besides those of water increase in number and complexity. Each problem, however important, must compete ever more urgently for attention, money, and manpower. This competition will make it that much more difficult to provide the resources needed to fulfill man's water requirements and demands.

Water poses a dual problem to man. First, a fixed amount—either national or global—has to do for increasing numbers of people wanting water for ever more uses; and second, because of the competition, the water must be made available at as low a cost and at the expenditure of as low a proportion of our total resources as possible. To solve these problems requires wise decisions and effective management.

Why is water so important? There are many reasons. These range from the role of water in the everyday process of living to the role of water in the evolution of life. This book is concerned with the management of water—how it is and must be handled to help people live, stay healthy, go about their business, and enjoy their leisure time. Water is important because it is necessary, useful, and convenient, because it is beautiful and restful, but, most of all, because it is necessary—to us, to our children, and to all future generations.

Besides air, nothing is more necessary to life than water. Without air, a man may die in two minutes and certainly will die in eight.

The Nile River has been Egypt's main highway for thousands of years.

THE WORLD'S WATER SUPPLY

About three-fourths of the earth is covered by fresh and salty water.

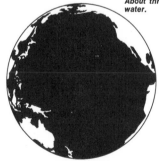

FRESH WATER: Only about 3 percent of all the earth's water is fresh.

ICE: Most of the fresh water — about 80 percent — is now frozen in ice caps and glaciers.

TOTAL AVAILABLE SUPPLY: The unfrozen fresh water — now in lakes and rivers, in the air and underground — is 20 percent of the total supply.

FRESH WATER IN LAKES, RIVERS, AND AIR: Excluding ground water, this amounts to no more than about 1½ percent (1/70) of all fresh water.

Without water, he will die in about four days. By contrast, provided that he has air and a little water, he can last for weeks without food. Each day, each of us uses about 5 to 6 quarts of water just living. Each day, somehow or other, each of us must replenish what he has used or dry out until he sickens and dies.

We need water also for our health—to keep ourselves, our homes, and our communities clean. One of the signs of a well-developed civilization is an adequate supply of clean water. The ancient Greeks located their cities near or around springs. Later the Romans built aqueducts that brought water many miles from distant mountains. At the height of its development, Rome provided about 50 gallons daily for each citizen. By contrast seventeenth-century Paris provided only 2½ quarts.

In the United States, enough water is taken from streams, lakes, wells, and springs to provide 100 gallons each day for each person for his domestic needs. The amounts range from a few gallons per day in some rural areas to more than 200 gallons in some southwestern cities. Considering all uses, public and private, domestic, industrial, and agricultural, a lavish 1,600 gallons per day is withdrawn from various sources for the average person in the United States. But two-thirds of the rural people of the world (and this includes some in the United States) and half of the city people outside the United States exist with inadequate, unhealthful water supplies.

Man uses water also to relax and to satisfy his need for quiet and beauty. Early Egyptian records speak of the pleasure of floating down the Nile. Writers, musicians, painters, and photographers have tried to capture the feeling of tranquillity that comes from seeing or being near water. Our national response to this need can be seen in the many lakes and rivers in our national, state, and local recreation and wilderness areas, parks, and forests. These provide places to fish and swim, places to boat and water-ski, and places just to watch the water.

Water is not only necessary to keep us alive and healthy, but also necessary to keep our economy going. It is needed to produce food and the hundreds of things that make our country and civilization what they are, and it is needed to flush away and dilute much of our waste. Nearly half the fresh water used annually in the United States is for the irrigation of crops. Every cow drinks about 3 gallons of

THE WATER BUDGET

The average yearly water budget, in inches, available in the 48 contiguous states (not including Alaska and Hawaii).

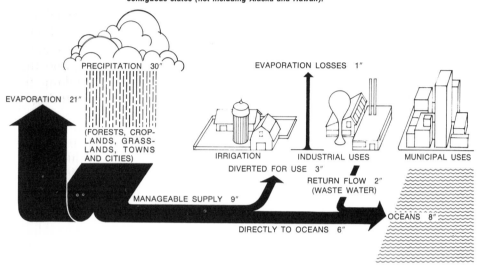

WATER BUDGET FOR THE 48 CONTIGUOUS STATES

INCOME	INCHES OF WATER	OUTGO
PRECIPITATION	30	
	−21	UNAVOIDABLE LOSS — Evaporation from all sources — forests, croplands, grass-lands, water surfaces, cities, towns, and roads.
Balance available for management, mostly in lakes, reservoirs, and rivers	9	
	−6	LOSS — Unused water flowing into the oceans.
BALANCE — Diversions for all uses, municipal, industrial, and agricultural	3	
	−2	LOSS — Waste water and return flows to the oceans.
	−1	LOSS — Evaporations during use.
NET ANNUAL SURPLUS OR DEFICIT	0	

water for every gallon of milk she gives. These 3 gallons do not include what the farmer uses to keep the cow and his dairy clean or what the processor uses to pasteurize the milk and to keep his machinery sanitary.

Almost as much water is used by industry and steam power plants as is used for the irrigation of crops, because most industrial and manufacturing processes require huge amounts of water. Although most people think an automobile needs water only in its radiator, it takes about 15,000 gallons of water to build an average car, and that doesn't include the tens of thousands of gallons used in making the ton or two of steel that goes into it. And to keep the car running, it takes 20 gallons of water to produce each gallon of gasoline.

Finally, we use water because it is convenient, it does things well, and it appears to be cheap. As a result, people use water as if there were no end to it, without regard for neighbor or future and, until recently, with little or no regard for the effects of this usage on the land and life around them.

Most people think flush toilets are the only kind there can be. Many cannot imagine living without automatic washers for clothes and dishes and disposal units for garbage. People in dry areas where water supplies are limited insist on houses with broad lawns. Farmers use familiar but outdated irrigation methods, wasting billions of gallons annually. Manufacturers use outmoded processes that require excessive amounts of water and produce vast quantities of waste which are dumped into streams and lakes, thus polluting them. Cities and farms use streams and lakes to dispose of sewage and dirt because "that's the way it's always been done." All these uses and

Irrigation made these California rice fields possible.

Three-fourths of the earth's fresh water is frozen in Antarctica.

practices, and many more, depend on fresh water because fresh water has been—and still is—plentiful, convenient, and traditional.

There would be little objection to most wasteful uses if the amount of water were unlimited. The sad fact is that it is not—neither in this country nor in the rest of the world.

Three-fourths of the earth's surface is covered by water, but the oceans, containing 97 percent of all water, are salty. Of the 3 percent of the total water that is fresh, about four-fifths is locked in ice caps and glaciers. Most of the ice is in Antarctica, Greenland, and other polar regions where it can't be used readily. What remains, estimated to be about five-eighths of 1 percent of the earth's total water supply, is all the fresh water there is for man's use all over the globe.

Although the percentage is small, our fresh-water supply still amounts to about 2,000,000 cubic miles. But not all *this* can be readily used. Ninety-eight and a half percent of all fresh water, other than that in the ice caps and glaciers, is in the ground, where it is hard to reach. The water in streams and fresh-water lakes available for easy use amounts to only 1½ percent of the 2,000,000 cubic miles of fresh water on earth.

Fortunately, the water in lakes, rivers, and streams is part of a grand system of circulation that operates all over the earth. Water evaporates from the oceans and lands and moves great distances with the air masses that cross and crisscross the earth. It falls mostly as rain or snow and then moves over the surface and through the ground

13

THE HYDROLOGICAL CYCLE

The circulation of water is continuous and irregular, rather than cyclic. All phases operate simultaneously, but at different rates in different places, and at different times.

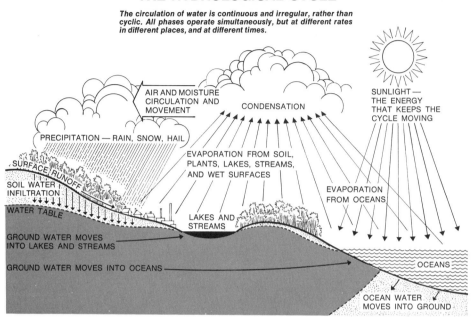

to return to the oceans. Except for the water in the ground (where movement generally is slow, usually in terms of feet per year), this circulation is rapid but variable. For example, the earth's rivers and streams contain a total of only about 300 cubic miles of water at any instant. However, rivers are replenished over and over again by rainfall, snowmelt, and seepage from water stored in the ground. As a result, their actual annual discharge is about 7,000 cubic miles. Roughly, then, the water in our streams is recirculated about twenty-five times each year. The 7,000 cubic miles represents about 10,000 gallons per person per day for a population of about 2½ billion people.

What about the United States? The records of the past hundred years or so show that enough rain and snow have fallen to cover the country—limited to simplify this discussion to the forty-eight contiguous states—to an average depth of 30 inches each year. This is about 1,500 cubic miles of water per year. More than two-thirds of this amount either evaporates from land and water surfaces or is transpired by trees, grass, other plants, and crops.

14

The remainder, about 420 cubic miles, is the most we can hope to manage at this time. This 420 cubic miles represents about 6,500 gallons per day for each of the approximately 200,000,000 people in the United States. Of this amount, about one-fourth is now being used, after which it too is evaporated or is returned to the streams and to the oceans. About three-fourths is never used. In fact, when water that is not used and water that is used and returned to the streams are counted, about 95 percent of the river water of the United States runs off into the oceans.

Although the figures given here are factual, they are deceptive because they are averages. Averages are arithmetical expressions which bring some degree of order into a large collections of numbers and make them easier to handle and understand. Averages, however, don't tell the real story; they are only calculated abstractions. To arrive at a national average, for example, the large differences in rain and snow between regions as unlike as the wet Northeast and the dry Southwest are lumped together. In an average, the true picture is masked, and the tragedy of droughts, the panic of floods, and the uncertainties of day-to-day supplies do not appear. Averages have their uses, but they do not describe real situations or real events.

We cannot use water "on the average." Within fairly narrow limits, we must make do with the water we have at a particular time in a particular place. It is how we make do within those limits that gives us a measure of our progress in managing our water resources. Man is not yet close to using all the water there is, but he is approaching—and in many places, including the United States, he has passed—the point where he is using all the water that is readily available. As a result, here in the United States, as in most populated parts of the world, more money, energy, and manpower than ever before will be required to provide the water people need to live, work, and enjoy themselves.

We can use water either wisely or foolishly, manage so that we can use it fully or mismanage so that we face one water crisis after another. In this book you will learn something of the background of water management. You will also learn of some ways in which those involved in water management are coping with today's problems. Lastly, you will find some guidelines for thinking about the water problems you will be facing for the rest of your life.

15

2

Before Water Management

When man was primarily a hunter, fisher, and gatherer of wild plant food, his need for water was small. Until about 30,000 years ago, man roamed in small scattered bands that stayed mostly in the open grasslands where the hunting was best. There he found water in adequate, if not abundant, quantities. Food and shelter were problems, but water was not, except in periods of drought. Within its own territory, a band knew every source of water, every stream, spring, and water hole. There was no way to carry or store water, so men seldom traveled more than a few hours from known water sources. These sources were used without being affected by men any more than they were by the animals who drank at the same spots.

Most water was drinkable. Although there were places where stream water was spoiled by a salty spring or where the water became salty by evaporation in a lake having no outlet, bad water was rare.

The Shaduf is still used to raise water in India.

The water early man used was not always pure by modern drinking standards, but man drank it and survived. Some rivers, like the Little Colorado in Arizona and the two Puercos in New Mexico, carried so much silt that even early man no doubt let it settle before he drank the water.

However, pollution existed to some extent even then. Animals and man polluted their watering places with their wastes. Plants and animals died and floated downstream to decompose somewhere on the bottom muds. Soil sloughed its compost of living and decaying matter into streams. Heavy rains added silt.

In general, however, the total amount of pollution was small, and streams and lakes were able to purify themselves naturally. Water absorbs air as it tumbles and flows downstream. The oxygen in the dissolved air reacts with most organic impurities—that is, those that come from plant and animal sources—to oxidize them. This process turns most organic pollutants into carbon dioxide and other materials that can either pass into the atmosphere or be absorbed by plants and simple forms of animal life. Under natural conditions stream and lake water contains enough dissolved oxygen to become clean within a few hundred yards of the point where the water was polluted. Streams also become purified because the pollution is diluted.

Favorable water conditions, however, did not exist everywhere even for early man. There were areas with not enough water and some with too much. On all continents there were—and still are— deserts where the rainfall is so low that water is always in short supply. Elsewhere, particularly in semideserts such as the Southwest, rainfall varies widely from year to year or from one period of years to another.

Thus, man has had to adjust to or avoid one or more of four basic water problems since earliest times. His supply has had to be of good quality, without too many dissolved salts or too much sediment. He has had to face floods or, on the other hand, learn to survive in deserts. Lastly, in some areas he has had to live with supplies that varied from year to year, with too much at some times and too little at others.

The four basic water problems exist because of conditions of climate, landforms, and types of rock that make up the terrain. These problems are natural—not man-made. In some instances, man can

18

make things worse. In a few places, he can—and has—made them better. In general, however, these problems involve natural forces so great that only in the past few decades has man been in a position to think about the possibilities of modifying them to his advantage.

Climate is the general year-round weather condition of a region. Although the weather changes from day to day, climate varies from year to year. Some years, for reasons not yet clearly understood, the air moving across the land contains either more or less moisture than usual. Large areas are subject to unexpected periods of flood or drought. These are comparatively short-term variations. Climate also varies over longer periods in intervals of a few tens to many thousands of years. Major changes in climate during the last million years resulted in five main ice ages and intervening periods of warmer weather.

The climate has continued to change slowly since the end of the last major retreat of ice about 12,000 years ago. Many scientists find evidence that the climate after the last ice age became warmer and drier until about 4,000 years ago. Since then it has again become cooler and moister. Today's climate is not that of an ice age, but then neither is it so warm and dry as it was about 2000 B.C. These long-term changes are too gradual to be sensed during any one man's life. This is largely because year-to-year fluctuations are so great that they mask the slow long-term trends. We know of them only through historical records, the work of scientists concerned with the past, and some extremely sensitive modern instruments and dating techniques.

Climate is not the only factor affecting the earth's water resources. They are also affected by movements of the earth's crust. Uplift, tilting, and subsidence of blocks of land change stream courses and coastlines. Mountains, as they are buckled upward, modify patterns of air circulation and precipitation. As landmasses rise, they are worn down and their debris is washed out to fill valleys, form deltas, and put layers of mud on the bottoms of lakes, estuaries, and oceans. The details of the features we see today became what they are only a few hundred to a few thousand years ago; even if left alone, they will not long remain as they are.

Not all natural changes are slow, however. The land can also change suddenly and drastically. In 1965 a volcano called Toal erupted in the Philippine Islands. In a few short days it spewed

19

Natural change: Volcanic eruption has destroyed this Philippine landscape.

cinders and ashes over several hundred square miles, changing a green productive region into gray, lifeless waste.

Landslides can also disrupt the landscape quickly, and they occur by thousands from one end of the country to the other. The Gros Ventre slide in Wyoming, which was triggered by an earthquake in 1927, formed a dam overnight. Behind it is a lake that may last hundreds of years. Sudden changes also occur when a lake tops its barriers and overflows. Such a change took place in eastern Washington, which contained part of a huge lake system that extended across Idaho into Montana during part of the ice ages. When the lake overflowed, which it did more than once, it sluiced out in what must have been among the great all-time floods. Left behind is a region so cut and slashed by the outpouring of water that today, thousands of years after the floods, it still deserves its name of the Scablands. Other sudden changes in the earth's surface have occurred when lava flows, pouring out in a few hours, have filled riverbeds, forcing the stream to cut new channels and find new outlets to the sea.

These and other natural catastrophes have effects of the same or greater orders of magnitude as do changes resulting from man-made dams, levees, canals, and other developments, about which we are so concerned. Our environment is changing constantly, either slowly or

20

Man-made changes: Canals pipe water through the Yuma sand dunes.

suddenly. So long as such changes occur naturally, it is not reasonable to expect man to refrain from making changes of his own. But it is reasonable to ask man to consider the long-range and side effects of the changes he plans to make.

Man changes his environment for specific benefits. For example, a dam is built to reduce flood hazards, regulate streamflow, or provide a dependable source of water for power production, city and industrial use, agriculture, and recreation. The benefits are easily visualized, and for short periods of time, for a few tens of years or a couple of centuries, the benefits may seem enormous. However, the benefits will last only until the dam fills with sediment—that is, if the dam doesn't break. Even while its benefits are being realized, a dam has unfavorable effects. The reduction of floods and regulation of streamflow at the same time reduces or eliminates the power of a stream to scour and clean its banks and bottom. These benefits also minimize or eliminate the use of floods to fertilize and rejuvenate the lands they inundate. The added weight of water in the reservoir behind the dam may cause local earthquakes. The reservoir covers lands that may have had other uses. At the mouth of the river, the balance of erosion and deposition and the balance of wildlife on shore and in the waters will be changed as the pattern of streamflow

21

Man-made and natural changes: A dam backs up a reservoir in the scablands (upper distance).

Ancient well

changes. Too often in the past, only the obvious benefits were considered in decisions to build dams.

Moreover, many man-made—and of course natural—changes are irreversible. Once a dam is built, neither the pattern of events downstream nor that upstream is ever the same again.

Consequently, man must think in terms of long-range and side effects as well as short-term benefits. He must consider and accept responsibility to prevent or alleviate undesirable consequences as part of the price of immediate benefits. This is not a simple matter, because it is not yet possible to predict *all* the ways in which nature adjusts to the changes man may impose on it. Too, nature commonly reacts slowly. Many effects may appear only after the planners and builders are long gone. The ones who will have to deal with the problems that show up only slowly may be the grandchildren, or even grandchildren of grandchildren, of the ones who enjoyed the benefits.

In each period of man's history, he has had to face some type of water problem. He began by adjusting his way of life to his water supplies and later developed ways to adjust his water supplies to his way of life. Perhaps the earliest form of management was the division of lands and water sources into territories controlled by bands, clans, or tribes. Each group knew the limits of its territory and protected its resources against poachers and invaders. In time, man learned to enlarge natural water holes and to dig new ones to store small supplies of water for emergencies. He also discovered that he could carry water with him in a gourd. The use of the gourd was a tremendous step forward. It gave man freedom to move from his source of water because he could carry water with him.

From this point on, the story of man is mainly the story of his learning how to manage his environment and, if possible, to control it. It is a story of magnificent successes and spectacular failures. It is the story of the rise and fall of civilizations. Central to the story, perhaps more important than battles and the succession of kings, is how civilizations learned, or failed to learn, to manage their water resources.

3

Our Problems Begin

Man did little to change his environment until he became a farmer, about 7,000 to 8,000 years ago. Until then his numbers were too few and too widely scattered. He did not have the tools or the skills to make many changes. When man began to bring land under his control, he took the first steps toward the civilizations, the increased population, and the water and pollution problems we have today.

Just how man progressed from the earliest planted fields to the first great civilizations we do not know. But by about 6,000 years ago he had learned in a few places how to bring water where and when he wanted it. His first major successes with managing water involved controlling its distribution for agricultural purposes. Some of these successes, however, later turned into failures because man had not yet learned the long-term consequences of disturbing the natural flow of water across the land.

WATER PROBLEMS

Areas of the 48 contiguous states of the United States where major water problems are common.

NATURAL WATER PROBLEMS

FLOODS

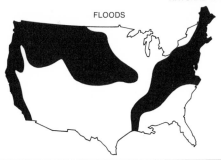

SHORT SUPPLY

UNDEPENDABLE SUPPLY

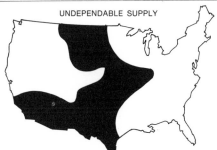

NATURALLY POOR QUALITY

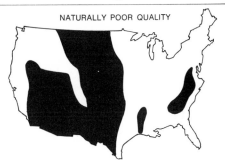

MAN-MADE OR MAN-AGGRAVATED PROBLEMS

DISTRIBUTION DIFFICULTIES

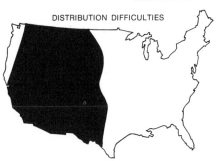

POLLUTION

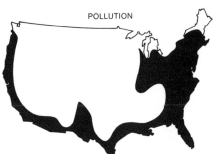

AREAS WITHOUT MAJOR WATER PROBLEMS

The earliest irrigation method, called flood irrigation, depended on a stream topping its banks and spreading out over the adjacent flats or floodplains. When the floodwaters receded, they left behind a thin film of rich silt and a soaked plain ready to be farmed. This type of irrigation occurs naturally, unaided and uncontrolled by man. Then man learned to build small dams to control some of the water. The earliest dams probably were low dikes made to hold back water that had overflowed onto the land so that it could soak into the ground before it ran off. By 5,000 years ago man had learned to build dams to raise the level of water and to distribute it through canals. Systems of dams and canals were developed along the Nile, the Tigris and the Euphrates, the Indus, and the Hwang Ho rivers.

Irrigation along the Nile depended on seasonal high water. After the flood had passed, the river levels dropped as much as 30 feet. Although the Egyptians didn't know it then, this drop allowed the Nile Valley to become the only one in the world that has been irrigated continuously from about 3000 B.C. to the present day. What the drop in river level did was to permit the soaked land to drain and the drainage to leach out, or remove, the various salts brought in by the floods. Had the salts accumulated in the soil instead of being leached out, in a few years the land would have become too full of salts to grow most crops.

The balance between the amount of salts added to the soil by irrigation and the amount leached out by drainage is known as the salt balance. If the balance is favorable, the soil remains sweet and continues to grow crops. If the balance is unfavorable, salts soon cause chemical changes in the soil that prevent good growth. This is one of the most important considerations in any irrigation system. The Egyptians didn't realize their luck.

Whether the Egyptians stay lucky remains to be seen. The high Aswan Dam across the Nile in southernmost Egypt and the smaller dams downstream now regulate the flow of the river. The Nile no longer rises and falls as it once did. Already the Egyptians are applying artificial fertilizer to areas where the river no longer deposits its yearly load of rich fertile mud. It is too soon yet to know the extent to which the controlled level of water has actually slowed the leaching of salts and reduced the fertility of the soil. An unexpected effect of controlling the annual floods is that the sardine catch in the

26

eastern Mediterranean Sea has dropped off about 95 percent because the sea is now deprived of flood-borne nutrients. Also, schistosomiasis, a highly debilitating disease, has increased greatly because the snails which carry the disease and thrive in water that flows steadily and slowly are no longer flushed out by annual floods.

Along the Tigris and Euphrates rivers, the ancient Sumerians were not so lucky. Their land was even flatter than that along the Nile, and the rise and fall of their rivers were smaller. Consequently drainage was also less effective. The Sumerians apparently irrigated a succession of large tracts of land along their rivers. Probably they moved from one area of sweet soil to another as their poorly drained lands built up their salt loads until crops couldn't grow.

We know also that the Sumerian civilization *disappeared.* One likely explanation for this is that their agricultural system collapsed. Some evidence suggests that unusually large floods cut such wide channels that succeeding normal floods could not rise high enough to top the banks and irrigate the adjacent fields. Unable to continue the agriculture that supported their flourishing cities, the Sumerians weakened and fell prey to marauders. The marauders, however, probably provided only the knockout blow. The body blows came from the silt and salt the Sumerians never learned to handle.

A similar story developed in North America at a much later time. In southern Arizona, ancient Indians who have been called the Hohokam developed an extensive irrigation system between about A.D. 800 and 1200. Without the help of draft animals they built canals as much as 40 feet wide and 125 miles long, and they irrigated as much as 50,000 acres. Why they stopped irrigating isn't certain, but there is evidence that it may have been due to an accumulation of salts in the soil or to waterlogging.

While learning how to manage the distribution of water, these ancient civilizations also developed laws to govern its use. Evidence suggests that water first was considered common property and divided on a "share and share alike" basis. A little later, in the semiarid areas around the Tigris and Euphrates rivers, water began to be distributed on the basis of "first in use, first in right," the so-called appropriation doctrine. Much later, water in Europe—a humid area—was distributed on the basis of land ownership, or what is known as riparian rights. This means that a man has the right to use the water

27

PREHISTORIC CANALS

Partial extent of prehistoric canals in the vicinity of Phoenix, Tempe, and Mesa, Arizona.

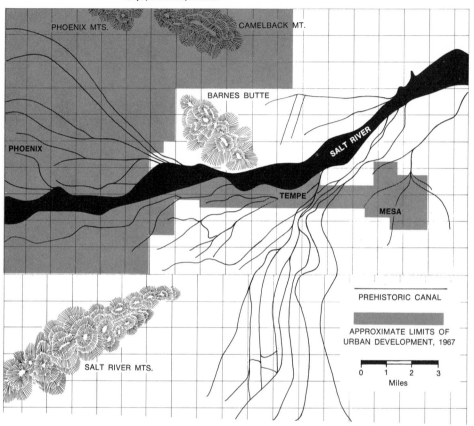

that flows over his land in any way he sees fit, provided he returns it to the stream essentially in the same condition as it was before he used it.

The appropriation doctrine was brought to North America by the Spaniards and still applies in many parts of the southwestern United States. The concept of riparian right was brought to the eastern seaboard of North America by the British. Often these concepts

Man has always needed to move water.
This aqueduct in Segovia, Spain, has been in use since Roman times.

governing rights to water use are applied side by side, particularly in the central and western United States. Streams large enough to be used by many people for many purposes are generally considered common property, but the rights to water of small streams are applied under riparian law or appropriation rights.

These legal concepts developed when communications were poor and sanitary conditions were crude. People neither knew nor cared what happened downstream and beyond the area in which they lived. As a result, people came to accept fouled streams as part of their way of living. The Tiber River below the Cloaca Maxima, the main sewer outlet of ancient Rome, was never a place to swim. In medieval Paris, early-morning churchgoers on their way to the Cathedral of Notre Dame covered their heads to shut off the smells of the Seine River. And the Thames River long ago became too dirty for commercial fishing. We have only recently begun to correct the damages caused by the traditional lack of concern for our neighbors' water.

With the coming of the Industrial Revolution in the late eighteenth and early nineteenth centuries, the need for water increased. The earliest major use of water was for power, but this was almost entirely nonconsumptive—that is, the use caused almost no increase in the amount of water lost naturally by evaporation.

As industry grew, the big problem quickly became pollution. A few farsighted men warned of the long-range danger of pollution to the natural environment in the early 1800's. But most people continued to hold their noses and not worry too much because, bad as things were, they were not too much worse than they always had been. Besides, industry brought jobs and money to the community. The economic consequences of the loss of industry not only frightened local businessmen, but often paralyzed the thinking of the community. Most communities preferred to think of industrial and municipal pollution as unfortunate but unavoidable rather than face the economic havoc that might be created by industry closing shop.

During the same general period, there was a tremendous surge of westward migration in North America. New regions were explored, and new lands were given over first to speculation and then to settlement. Agriculture and industry boomed, following the westward push of the railroads. Man grew confident, even cocky, of his ability

30

to manage his environment. Rivers were dammed to make them navigable and bridged to connect opposite banks. Forests were cleared, and prairies were turned into farms. There seemed to be no end to what man could do.

One result that no one expected was erosion. Rivers always carry some sediment—particles of sand, silt, and clay that are picked up by water as it moves over the ground. However, more particles are eroded from bare ground than from covered areas. Forests and grasslands contribute only a little sediment to our streams; agricultural land, a little more; and cutover forests, a great deal more. But the most is contributed by row crops, strip mining, and the building of houses, shopping centers, factories and roads.

In the middle 1930's great efforts were made to reduce erosion from agricultural and cutover forest land. Many of the adopted

Cracks in canal walls, caused by subsidence

Land collapse caused by removal of ground water

techniques, such as contour plowing, were highly successful. Similar measures have yet to be applied with the same degree of effectiveness to the tremendous erosion resulting from stripping land to build cities and roads and to operate mines. One of the most disastrous effects of inadequate planning for erosion is landsliding in residential areas, as occurs frequently in southern California.

In the middle 1800's, people knew so little about the environment of the Great Plains that speculators enticed thousands of farmers into that dry open country with the cry "Rain follows the plow!" and the government encouraged settlement with the Homestead Act. By coincidence, for a time they were right because a succession of wet years produced good crops. Hardly anyone suspected those wet years were wetter than normal—for there were no weather records. Only a handful believed the warnings of the few old-timers acquainted with the plains that these were not years of normal rainfall. When the dry years came in the 1880's, many farmers went broke. Many others, however, began to experiment with and use the conservation and managerial techniques that are now a part of modern farming methods. Today the Great Plains region is mostly prosperous farming country again, and modern techniques permit the best use of the available water. Even so there are good years and bad.

Modern technology, farmers and developers found, is not cheap. Most of the money to support the massive irrigation and flood-control projects necessary to save the region came from the rest of the country through federal support. As a result, the Missouri Basin today contains one of the largest multipurpose irrigation and power systems in the world. The region has now developed nearly all its surface-water resources, and its ground-water resources are over-pumped in some places. Continuing development will require careful planning and management of existing water supplies and those that may be imported in the future.

As population and cities grew and as industry and agriculture expanded, the water problem that increased in importance faster than any other was pollution. Someone has said that each time he sees a trainload of freight cars heading for a city he visualizes an equally long freight train of garbage and trash moving out—to be dumped in lakes, rivers, and the sea. Many of our lakes and rivers are already so foul that we realize we cannot continue to dump our wastes into them without polluting them beyond repair. The problems of water management today and for the future are to clean up our waters and keep them clean, while taking advantage of moving water's ability to dilute and dispose of waste and to make certain that everyone has the water he needs. To do these jobs simultaneously, in balance with the other physical aspects of our environment, and as cheaply and as well as possible, is no easy task.

Self-propelled field sprinkler irrigates crops.

The steel industry uses enormous quantities of water.

Subsidence: Land has dropped three feet below original level of pump.

4

Water Management Becomes Necessary

Today's water problems are not new—they are just bigger and more complicated than ever before. There are two reasons for this. The first is that the number of people has increased. Problems that once were local and small are now regional or international and tremendous. The second is that standards of living are rising. More people are earning more money, and industry and commerce are making efforts to provide everyone with what he wants or can afford. This results in both increasing demands for clean water and increasing capacities to pollute it.

So far as anyone can foresee, the situation is not going to get much better in the near future. Populations are expected to increase for at least another few decades, cities will grow, industry will need more water, and water problems will become more and more difficult. The magnitude of the increase can be visualized in terms of the present

36

Fish killed by detergents, industrial waste, and other pollutants ...

rate of growth of the world's population. The present rate of increase
is about 70,000,000 people per year. This is more than one-third of
the population of the United States and more than three times the
population of Canada. Nonetheless there is reason for hope. As the
problems have become more severe, people and governments have
speeded their efforts to learn more about water and do something
about it. Today public and private interests are cooperating as never
before to pool what is known and to improve our understanding of

wash up on the banks of the Potomac.

how to work together to solve our water problems.

The task of water management is to use what is known about water to provide the public with the water it is willing to pay for. It is also a task of water management to make certain that we continue learning more about our environment so that we can manage and adjust to it wisely. As our use of the environment becomes more complex, we must learn more in order to be able to develop more capable and sophisticated techniques. It is only because we have increased our

39

knowledge over the preceding years that we are able to analyze the existing water problems as well as we can and can hope to manage them with some degree of wisdom.

The water problems facing the public and the men selected to provide the public with water—the water managers—can be grouped into six categories. Four represent the interrelationships of land and climate. These are floods, perennial shortages of supply, undependable and irregular supplies, and naturally poor quality. The last two exist naturally but become acute because of man's activities. In order to live in and develop areas of undependable and irregular supply, water is moved to where it can be best used without harming its area of origin. Thus distribution becomes a major problem in areas of short and irregular supply and in adjacent areas which are called on to provide water out of their surpluses. Pollution, resulting from old-fashioned or poorly managed disposal of the huge quantities of waste produced by practically everything man does, is superimposed on all regions and all problems except in the few areas where population is small and where the water supplies are ample.

In dealing with these problems, water managers have six general objectives. The first is to regulate streamflow. The aim of regulation is to provide enough water at the right time and place for irrigation, navigation, municipal, industrial, and recreational purposes. It involves the building of dikes and dams, the regulation of lakes and reservoirs to control floods, and the protection of cultivated and other areas from excessive erosion.

A second objective is to improve water quality. This includes learning how to handle, purify, and use waste products. It also includes learning how to control the amounts and types of sewage, waste, and heat that are dumped into our waters.

A third objective of water managers is to improve the ways in which water is used. They seek to develop new and better techniques so that given supplies of water can be used and reused several times before they flow into the ocean or are evaporated. The more we can *reuse* water, the more we in effect increase our available water supply.

The fourth major objective is concerned with ground water. Ground water is the water that seeps into and moves slowly through the ground to considerable depths. It forms a tremendous emergency

Desalting plant, Florida

reserve supply for the nation. The amount of water in the ground is more than fifty times the amount available on the surface. Although the storage capacity of the ground is large, ground water is replenished at a rate that is only a fraction of the annual runoff to streams. To use the large storage capacity of the ground without dangerously depleting the reserve or causing related undesirable effects is one of the great challenges to water management.

The fifth objective is to find ways of adding to supplies available from surface and ground-water sources. At present, studies are concentrating on desalting salty water, modifying the weather to make more rain, and reducing evaporation losses to preserve water in reservoirs or to increase runoff.

The sixth and last objective is to improve methods of distributing water on local, regional and continental scales, without irreparably damaging the areas involved. Every improvement that can be made adds that much water to the amount that is available for use.

Checking back, you will see that no one of the objectives of water management attacks only a single water problem. The reason is that each of management's objectives involves or affects all, or nearly all, the problems. For example, if a river is regulated, it provides a more dependable supply for cities and farms and for the production of power. The regulation also helps control floods and provides a more constant river level, which is a help to navigation and recreation. People like to go to the river without worrying whether it will be so

41

Before water management the Tennessee River at Knoxville often looked like a big mud puddle. Year-round navigation was impossible.

The completion of TVA's Fort Loudoun Dam created a deepwater, all-year channel for navigation.

shallow that they can't water-ski or so high that the boat docks are underwater or destroyed.

Regulation also may bring unexpected problems. If a stream is regulated, as the Egyptians may learn in the near future when the Aswan Dam has operated a few years, the adjacent fields will not be so well drained because of more constant river levels. A regulated stream also is partly like a pond and flows at a steadier rate than an unregulated stream. Consequently pollution tends to build up more rapidly than it would if an occasional small flood sluiced it downstream. The reduced rate of flow also lessens the amount of air dissolved in the water and lets temperatures rise. These changes affect fish and other river life and slow down the natural cleansing action of the stream.

It took a long time for people working with water problems to realize that all aspects of water had to be considered when dealing with any one problem. The Sumerians, for example, learned how to deal mainly with their central problem—to bring water to their land—and as a result their fields were buried by an accumulation of silt and salt and their cities and civilization stagnated and disappeared. Similarly, some of the earliest dams in the modern era were built only to produce electric power or provide flood control. This practice soon came to a halt because the dams cost too much to be used only for one purpose, and multiple-purpose dams began to be designed. This means that the water behind the dam is planned to be used for power, irrigation and municipal water supplies, recreation, flood control, and the improvement of navigation.

Today even multiple-purpose planning isn't enough. It is necessary also to look ahead and plan for the industrial, agricultural, and municipal developments that will use the water. Consider just one common use for the water of a multiple-purpose dam—irrigation. Today planning for new irrigation projects requires planning for the processing of crops produced by the irrigation, for communities of people to farm and process the crops, and for the distant markets that will use the products. There simply is no end to the ways in which managing our water resources affects all aspects of our life. Water management must consider all phases—supply, use, reuse, and, finally, disposal of the unusable remainder. It must consider the future as well as the present.

5

Management and Conflicting Interests

With every aspect of our lives affected by what we do with our water, it should come as no surprise that sometimes the people who want water for different purposes end up in conflict with each other. At one time people shot it out over their water holes. Today they may go to court or to their legislatures. Good water management can make itself felt here by providing the facts by which judges, legislators, and the public can make their decisions. At least this can be done where the facts are available. Too often, however, we do not yet know enough to make all our decisions wisely for both the near and the distant future.

Let's take an extreme but comparatively simple example of different views regarding water. The Green River runs through a spectacular gorge that spans the Colorado-Utah boundary. Downstream from the gorge are large acreages that could be irrigated more effectively if

THE WATER MANAGER'S PROBLEM WORLD

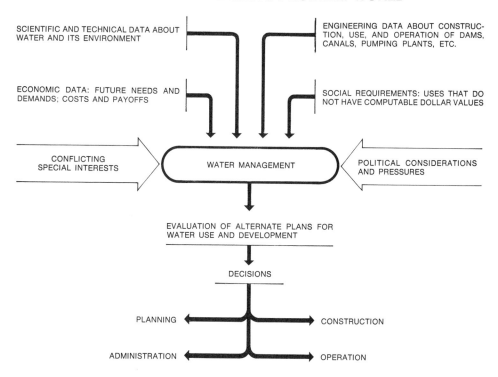

SCIENTIFIC AND TECHNICAL DATA ABOUT WATER AND ITS ENVIRONMENT

ENGINEERING DATA ABOUT CONSTRUCTION, USE, AND OPERATION OF DAMS, CANALS, PUMPING PLANTS, ETC.

ECONOMIC DATA: FUTURE NEEDS AND DEMANDS; COSTS AND PAYOFFS

SOCIAL REQUIREMENTS: USES THAT DO NOT HAVE COMPUTABLE DOLLAR VALUES

CONFLICTING SPECIAL INTERESTS

WATER MANAGEMENT

POLITICAL CONSIDERATIONS AND PRESSURES

EVALUATION OF ALTERNATE PLANS FOR WATER USE AND DEVELOPMENT

DECISIONS

PLANNING

CONSTRUCTION

ADMINISTRATION

OPERATION

there were a more dependable supply of water. A growing mining and manufacturing center near Salt Lake City could expand with additional electrical power. The people in favor of encouraging new developments urged the building of a dam and reservoir in the gorge. However, as soon as the proposal was made, other people claimed that the dam and reservoir would destroy the natural beauty of the gorge. The gorge, they claimed, should be preserved for future generations to enjoy.

Those who wished to preserve the gorge argued that it was a national heritage and should be left in its natural state. Those who wished to dam the gorge argued that it would be a public benefit to develop the downstream area. Which group was right? There is no way today to provide a clear-cut answer. Under our present system the critical question is which group can muster the greatest public support.

In 1956 the people who wanted to preserve the area won their battle in Congress, and Dinosaur National Monument, which includes the gorge, remains in its natural state as a part of our National Park System. How long will it be before the issue is raised again? We cannot tell, but unless other sources of water and power are found in the region, we can be certain that it will be. According to the current decision of Congress, the area remains available for future development. If a dam had been built and water had backed up behind it, the gorge could never again have been the same.

The Green River case also points up the two major ways in which the use of water is determined. The first is by the nature of water and its environment. In this case the water was in a rugged area of natural beauty while the mineral deposits and cultivatable lands were nearby in areas where water was in short supply. The second is by how people think about water and how they want to use it and its environment. People consider water from many different points of view and also have many mistaken ideas about its occurrence and use. Often the way people think about water creates more difficulties for the water manager than do the nature of water and its distribution.

As the Green River conflict showed, some people want to preserve nature for man's enjoyment and others want to use it to improve man's economic welfare. These two large groups, which often oppose each other in regard to water development, are themselves made up of many smaller groups. And the smaller groups do not always agree among themselves. For example, people who wish to preserve wilderness areas generally work with those who enjoy outdoor recreation. In the case of the Green River, however, the recreationists sided with the developers. They wanted the reservoir to provide an area for boating, camping, fishing, and water skiing in a region where opportunities for such activities are rare. The preservationists wanted the gorge left strictly alone.

The people who supported the dam for economic development also had their troubles. Others interested in different aspects of development questioned the need to harness the Green River for more power and more irrigation. Was the new dam worth the expense, they

46

The Green River sparked a controversy in water management.

The Green River provides recreational facilities.

asked, if it put existing power plants out of business? Did the nation really need a new irrigated area when it was already struggling with crop surpluses? Were the new dam and its associated works the best way to spend the money at that time? Congress also apparently questioned the need for the dam and eventually decided to preserve the gorge in its natural state rather than to develop the water supply.

Among the things which make water management difficult is that people believe that water should be cheap—either that or free. The water manager knows that today water cannot be cheap, but he also knows that if he doesn't make it *appear* to be cheap, he may be

48

voted or forced out of office. Across the country, the price of water generally ranges between 20 cents and $1 per 1,000 gallons. The average family uses about 3,000 gallons per month. New Yorkers brag about how they pay a small fixed price for water no matter how much they use. However, the few dollars each family or user pays per month for water is only a small part of the total cost of bringing the water to their taps. The difference is made up through taxes.

Moreover, because everyone thinks the water is cheap, many use it wastefully. The waste increases taxes, and the increase is paid by all, not just those who waste the water. It has been estimated that the 8,000,000 people in New York City use 1 billion gallons per day, of which they *waste* 200,000,000 to 300,000,000 gallons each day. In contrast, the 7,000,000 people in London, where water is metered, *use* only 420,000,000 gallons. People must learn the real cost of water so that they will use it prudently and will insist that others do the same.

A sidelight on the water-cost issue is the practice by many cities of decreasing the price of water as the amount used increases. This is done mainly to accommodate large industrial users. The cost may be 50 cents per 1,000 gallons for the first 10,000 gallons, then 40 cents per 1,000 for the next 20,000, and so on. This pricing practice makes sense when selling manufactured products where volume production reduces cost per unit, but with water it does not. The more water a city uses, the larger, more widespread, and more expensive its system becomes. Reducing costs for users of large amounts of water means that they benefit at the expense of the small user.

Sometimes problems are magnified because people take their water-using habits with them when they move to a different region. A clear example is in the semiarid southwestern states. The people who move from the humid East into Arizona, for example, think they should be able to use water in the same way they used it before. They make little concession to the fact that they have moved from areas having 25 to 50 inches of rain each year to those that have only about 5 to 15 inches. They build dams and huge canals and sink thousands of wells into the ground so that they can have as much water for farming as fell as rain in the wet East. Crops are grown not so much because they are adapted to dry conditions but because of the profit they bring. Sometimes some crops are irrigated whether they need water or not. Most houses have lawns, and grass needs several times

49

the amount of water that falls as rain. Because of the heavy demand for water, many ground-water reserves are being depleted, and in many places the ground itself has begun to crack and sink, or subside. Subsidence occurs because of excessive removal of water from the ground by pumping or by the application of water to certain kinds of clays that compact drastically after being soaked.

One consequence of such misuse is that the costs of delivering water are too great to be carried alone by the people who are its users and immediate beneficiaries. As a result, much of the construction for water supplies in many of our western areas is supported heavily by the federal government. This means that the money comes from taxes that are paid by all citizens, not just those in the western states. The justification for this is that the rest of the country benefits from the development of what would otherwise be tremendous unused tracts of land.

Many incorrect ideas about water have ended up being part of our laws. In part this is to be expected, for many of our laws were written when the nature of water was less well understood than it is now. Water, however, is largely governed by natural, not by man-made, laws. The basic natural laws, we are learning, are pretty straightforward. Gravity makes water move generally downhill, and the second law of thermodynamics prescribes that moving water follows the easiest route possible. Many legal disputes have resulted because man-made laws were written without consideration for the natural laws. These disputes have made life difficult for water users, though profitable for consultants and lawyers.

In Arizona, for example, use of ground water is governed largely on the basis of property law. A farmer is permitted to pump all the water he needs from his existing wells. If he needs more water, as when his wells begin to falter in their production, he may increase the capacity of the pumps, or deepen his wells, or even replace them. He may not, of course, drill a new well on his neighbor's property just to increase his supply. That would be an infringement of his neighbor's rights, unless he made the proper legal and financial settlements. However, what the law does not make allowances for is that he can legally use his neighbor's ground water almost to the same extent by increasing the amount of water his wells produce by deepening them or increas-

Green River water could be used to expand industry in downstream areas

... and to increase irrigated farmland on this undeveloped plain.

Copper mining uses water from the adjacent mountains at every stage.

ing the size of their pumps. By increasing the amount he pumps, the ground water is drawn from an ever-widening volume of ground around the well. This ever-widening volume, called the cone of depression, eventually reaches across the imaginary downward extension of his property lines to draw water out from under his neighbor's property. Suits over such situations are common and are not always decided consistently. What the law does not yet formally recognize is that ground water moves without regard to property lines or property laws. To apply property law to the movement of water under the ground makes about as much sense as to apply it to the movement of wind across its surface.

Fortunately our laws are improving. Lawmakers and judges are learning that no law or decision concerning the use of water can be a good one unless it takes into consideration the natural laws that govern the movement of water. Among water managers' tasks are the responsibilities to keep operations within the spirit and letter of existing laws and at the same time to conduct their work realistically. When the two objectives prove to be incompatible, water managers strive for legal regulations that are consistent with the ways water actually moves through its environment.

In the past few years, pollution and water supply problems have become so evident that people realize more than ever how greatly water affects them. Many communities and regions are facing the need to make decisions that will cost large sums. Although people are becoming increasingly aware that the decisions they make will affect their water resources for many years, if not irrevocably, they often continue to value water for many conflicting and sometimes unrealistic reasons. Water managers have an important responsibility to keep the public informed regarding the costs, benefits, and disadvantages of alternate plans for using water.

The managers also have the responsibility to see that our understanding of water and its environment stays ahead of the complexity of our water problems. Today's problems are solved with what was learned yesterday. Tomorrow's problems will be solved by what is learned today. New information, knowledge, and understanding of the interrelationships of physical, chemical, social, economic, and political conditions must be acquired and passed on continuously to the public. It is the only sound basis on which the public and water managers can make the decisions for which the public has to pay.

6

Droughts in a Tradition of Plenty

Everyone knows what drought means in general, yet no one can define it to everyone's satisfaction. In this book, drought is used to denote a period of unusually prolonged dry weather. But even this definition does not have the same meaning everywhere. In desert areas no one talks about a drought until months or even years go by without the few expected rains. In humid areas, by contrast, a few dry weeks or sometimes just a few rainless days, and everyone talks about a drought. Actually even a few weeks of below-normal rainfall in a wet area can bring on a real crisis.

In this chapter you will learn how two humid areas, New York City and southern Florida, reacted to droughts. Keep in mind that as yet there is nothing we can do about controlling droughts. The best that can be done now is to learn how to manage the water resources we have, in order to contend successfully with droughts when they occur.

Hammock and stream patterns in the Everglades

New York City and its metropolitan area lie in the northeastern United States, where rainfall, snowfall, and streamflow are generally plentiful. The principal natural water problem is floods. And yet for the 5 years between 1961 and 1966, this region experienced a drought that had no equal in its recorded history. Nothing in about 150 years of water records or in the historical writings of the preceding 200 years suggested any drought of such magnitude. There had been many disastrous floods, but droughts? Just a few dry spells—nothing really to worry about.

Up to the early 1800's, New York obtained its water from shallow and often polluted wells. In 1832 the city began to reach out into the nearby rural areas to obtain water for its growing population. By 1890 it had to extend its water sources 40 miles to the Croton River watershed, and this too soon proved insufficient. Then, in the early 1900's, the water-supply system was extended to collect water from the Ashokan Basin in the Catskill Mountains about 120 miles away. The Ashokan plan was a farsighted one. Between 1900 and 1960 New York's population grew from 4,000,000 to about 8,000,000. Until the drought of 1961–66, the system that brings water from Ashokan, with comparatively few small expansions, had been adequate to take care of the growing water demands.

During all this time New York City had the flow of the Hudson River going past its front doors. However, the Hudson was polluted, and New York's water managers believed it would be better to go a long way for clean water than to treat the water from the Hudson to make it fit for municipal use. Besides, until recently the available treatment methods were inadequate to provide the quality of water that was desired at a reasonable cost.

At the end of two years of drought the farmers in the rural areas began to worry. At the end of three years many towns and cities were declaring water emergencies, and after the fourth year the federal government stepped in to provide disaster relief. Even in the fifth year there was no way to know the drought would not go into its sixth. Not until the spring of 1967 could anyone say for certain that there had been enough rain and snow the preceding winter to overcome the shortage and that the drought was over, at least temporarily.

What were some of the steps taken to ease the effects of the drought? What about the future?

For three years the effects of the drought were absorbed by the reserves built into New York City's water system. But by 1965 the reserves were so low that the use of water had to be restricted. Limits were set on use of water for air conditioning, automobile washing, and lawn sprinkling. Many communities repaired leaky water mains and pipelines. All these measures helped. Many restaurants even stopped serving water unless their customers specifically asked for it. This measure didn't save much water, but it received lots of publicity and made the public more aware of its water problems.

The people of New York City had a particularly hard time. Because water for domestic use in most of the New York area is not metered, the people were not used to being careful with it.

Another part of the problem involved Philadelphia. Part of New York City's water supply comes from the upper part of the drainage basin of the Delaware River, which, farther downstream, provides Philadelphia with most of its water supply. Whenever the flow of the Delaware is low, Philadelphia has the problem of keeping the brackish—or moderately salty—water of Delaware Bay from moving up the river to the intake pipes that collect water for the city's supply. At the time New York City developed its water supply in the upper Delaware Basin, an agreement was reached with Philadelphia. New York would release 200,000,000 gallons daily whenever the water was needed to build up the flow in the Delaware. This increased flow would hold the movement of brackish water short of Philadelphia's intakes. During the last part of the drought, New York City balked at providing water under the agreement because of its own need. For a few days it looked as if there would be serious trouble similar to that over water holes in the old West. However, an agreement was finally reached, and New York City arranged to fulfill its commitment.

Pollution problems also worsened during the drought. Although sewage and industrial waste continued to be produced at undiminished rates, there was less water to flush and dilute them. Little was done about this.

Fortunately, the drought ended before New York's municipal and industrial services had to be severely curtailed. During the drought, water managers could do little except try to find additional sources of water and ask people to cut back on use and wastage. The water managers are now seeking ways to protect the city against similar experiences in the future. What can be done?

57

First, better use can be made of the water supply the city has. Its distribution system, which is one of the leakiest of any large city, can be repaired. Remember the figures comparing New York's waste with London's use. The public and industries can be educated to be more careful in their use of water. Meters can be installed. Reconditioning and reuse of water wherever possible can be encouraged or even required. This is already being done with water for air conditioning.

Second, the city water managers can look for additional supplies. This is easier said than done because almost all nearby basins have their surface water claimed already. However, the use of ground water, which has not been exploited to the same degree as surface water, could be increased for the duration of emergencies. Desalting ocean and brackish water has also been urged. In fact, New York City is considering a nuclear desalting plant as a reliable source of supply during future emergencies. But about a billion gallons per day are used in the city. Therefore, a real crisis would not be averted by the 25,000,000-gallon-per-day capacity of the proposed emergency desalting plant. Nonetheless, the presence of the plant would reassure many people. Perhaps its extraordinary cost, compared to the cost of obtaining an equal amount of water from conventional sources, is justified as a way to make people realize the high cost of water misuse.

Some people have even suggested blocking Long Island Sound at both ends, flushing out the sea water, and making the Sound a tremendous fresh-water reservoir. Although this suggestion is visionary, fishing and sailing enthusiasts have already voiced objections.

But it isn't necessary for New York water managers to look farther out into the country for water or to install expensive and inadequate desalting plants or to turn Long Island Sound into a reservoir. New York has an adequate water supply rolling right past its waterfront. The Hudson River alone can supply all of New York's needs. Although the Hudson is polluted, techniques are now available to clean up the water to acceptable standards. Treatment would be expensive, but perhaps no costlier than developing new sources, especially if upstream pollution is reduced as required under the Federal Water Pollution Control Act.

There is another approach to a solution, which would be realistic but certainly not popular. The 1961–66 drought was unpleasant, but

PREVENTING CONTAMINATION OF GROUND WATER

Dams in drainage canals prevent salt water from contaminating fresh ground water.

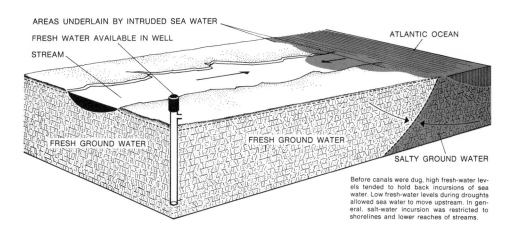

AREAS UNDERLAIN BY INTRUDED SEA WATER

FRESH WATER AVAILABLE IN WELL

STREAM

ATLANTIC OCEAN

FRESH GROUND WATER

FRESH GROUND WATER

SALTY GROUND WATER

Before canals were dug, high fresh-water levels tended to hold back incursions of sea water. Low fresh-water levels during droughts allowed sea water to move upstream. In general, salt-water incursion was restricted to shorelines and lower reaches of streams.

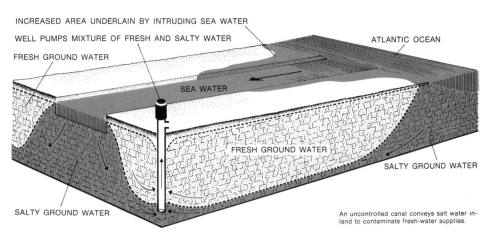

INCREASED AREA UNDERLAIN BY INTRUDING SEA WATER

WELL PUMPS MIXTURE OF FRESH AND SALTY WATER

FRESH GROUND WATER

ATLANTIC OCEAN

SEA WATER

FRESH GROUND WATER

SALTY GROUND WATER

SALTY GROUND WATER

An uncontrolled canal conveys salt water inland to contaminate fresh-water supplies.

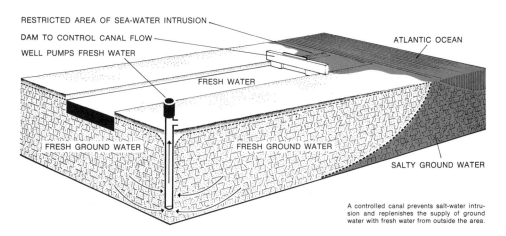

RESTRICTED AREA OF SEA-WATER INTRUSION

DAM TO CONTROL CANAL FLOW

WELL PUMPS FRESH WATER

ATLANTIC OCEAN

FRESH WATER

FRESH GROUND WATER

FRESH GROUND WATER

SALTY GROUND WATER

A controlled canal prevents salt-water intrusion and replenishes the supply of ground water with fresh water from outside the area.

most people survived with comparatively little discomfort. Perhaps the most reasonable thing to do is to plan to accept some degree of discomfort when the next drought comes. In this way the tax money could be used for something more necessary than a hedge against an uncertain drought at an unknown date.

The decision on which course or combination of courses to take is one the public must make with the help of the best possible advice from its water managers. Regardless of what New York City's people decide to do, one thing is certain—the water in their future is going to be more expensive than the water in their past. The best possible water management will be needed to keep these costs down as far as reasonable, to educate New Yorkers to use their water supplies more efficiently, and to provide the city with adequate supplies for all purposes.

Let's look south. Southern Florida is one of the flattest, wettest areas in the United States. The average rainfall, nearly twice that of the average for the forty-eight contiguous states, ranges from about 45 to 70 inches per year, and the land is so flat that water can run off only slowly. As a result, the ground is nearly waterlogged. Lake Okeechobee, in the central part of southern Florida, is only 14 feet above sea level, and the sea is from about 25 to 100 miles away. The slope of the land from Lake Okeechobee to the edge of the sea is so slight that if southern Florida were the size of an ordinary desk, the top not only would look flat, but would feel polished to your fingertips.

Rainfall around Lake Okeechobee averages about 55 inches per year. More than three-fourths of a year's rain falls from June to October. As the rain soaks into the ground, the water in the ground rises toward the surface and fills the lake. Before the region was developed, when Lake Okeechobee finally spilled over, a great shallow river would start moving slowly toward the sea. By late fall as much as 80 percent of the region south of the lake would be flooded. This periodically flooded region formed what is called the Everglades. After the rains, the river kept draining slowly toward the sea. As the dry months continued, the water in the ground sank, and much of the water remaining on the surface seeped into the ground but left much of the land marshy. The following spring and early

Airboats patrol the Everglades

summer the rains would come again, and the cycle would be repeated.

Such annual cycles have been going on in the Everglades for about 5,000 years. Today southern Florida has a unique environment in which plants and animals are adjusted to a cycle that depends on late-summer rains, the rise and fall of water in the ground, and the sluggish movement of water through the Everglades. The cycle described, however, is of average conditions. Like all averages, it is made up of nonaverage conditions. Floods and drought also are part of the natural sequence of events in the Everglades. Hurricanes in 1926 and 1947 poured so much water on and through the Everglades that it seemed that nothing could survive. At other times, six-week to four-month droughts, which are considered severe, have dried up water holes, let sea water move upstream to kill fresh-water fish and plants, and have starved most of the large birds and animals. In addition, dozens of lightning-strike fires have burned across thousands of acres of dry grassland, destroying plants and animals.

Nonetheless, the Everglades have survived. After each seeming catastrophe, as floods receded or droughts gave way to reviving rains, the grass came back, and with it the teeming complex of life.

In 1947 part of the area was declared the Everglades National Park. The National Park System is aimed to conserve unique natural environments as a heritage for the benefit and enjoyment of the people of the United States. This objective has been a difficult one to achieve in the Everglades and one that has not yet been completely achieved. The problem is people—not in the Everglades, but in the adjoining parts of southern Florida.

Long before Florida was discovered by Ponce de Leon in 1513, the Everglades was occupied by Indians. These early Indians lived by hunting, fishing, and gathering shellfish, and they lived without greatly disrupting the environment. In the late-eighteenth and early-nineteenth centuries the Seminole Indians moved into the area under pressure from the expanding colonies and states. In the Everglades they found a difficult environment, but they adjusted to it and survived.

The time of general wilderness for southern Florida ended at the close of the nineteenth century when the first railroad was pushed down the east coast. The town of Miami was born. Land speculators began to publicize the virtues of the rich flat organic soils for farming and of the coastal area for retirement and recreation. The people who came were not content to adjust to the land and its water cycles. They came to develop the land, and to do this they had to control its water.

The land was not easy to develop. It was so wet that it had to be drained to grow crops; the first drainage canal was built in 1906. Twenty years later, about 440 miles of canal had been dug, and miles of levees had been raised around Lake Okeechobee to keep its floods under control. The early drainage canals were not big or numerous enough to take care of large floods, yet when droughts occurred, they proved to be big enough to drain the land until it dried out, cracked, and subsided. In some places the dried soil settled as much as 8 feet. During wet seasons many sunken areas became lakes. This ruined many farming enterprises.

During the same period, Miami and other cities along the east coast continued to grow and to demand ever-increasing amounts of water. In 1945 the coastal area was using about 150,000,000 gallons of water per day. By 1965 the use had doubled. Where did these supplies come from? Surface runoff is too erratic for dependable supplies, and the country is too flat to build dams for reservoirs. The water came from the ground. Southeastern Florida is underlain by one of the world's most productive aquifers—formations of rock that contain water that can be pumped readily out of the ground.

This aquifer contains tremendous quantities of water, but it could not supply all the water required by both the cities and the farmers while it also was being drained continuously by losses of water that cut into it. As uncontrolled drainage continued and pumping increased, ground-water levels fell. This set the stage for a new complication. As the water levels dropped near the east coast and along the canals, sea water moved inland up the drainage canals and into the aquifer, where it contaminated the fresh water for both the cities and the farmers. Extensive study and experimentation showed how this contamination by sea water could be controlled. Fresh water could be added to the aquifer and the salt water kept out of the canals by means of adjustable concrete and steel barriers. In dry weather the barriers keep the level of fresh water up and hold back the incursion of sea water. They also control the flow of fresh

The Hudson River carries enough water to satisfy New York's needs, if it were properly treated.

AQUIFERS

Aquifers are water-saturated bodies of rock that yield water to wells in useful quantities. The top of the water-saturated zone forms the water table. When water tables are high, aquifers contain more water, and when water tables are low, aquifers contain less. This is why ground-water users are troubled by low or falling water levels.

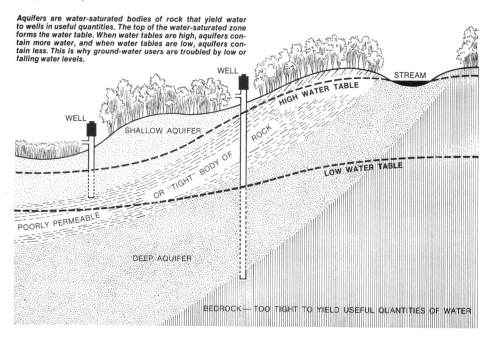

water from the canals and delay runoff by diverting some of it to special impoundments. Fresh water is added to the aquifer by induced recharge—that is, by runoff that is held back so that there is time for it to seep into the ground. By being diverted to canals and held in the special areas, the movement of water through the Everglades and out to sea was greatly modified. The adjustable dams are opened in wet weather so that the canals can carry off excess water and prevent flooding of the land.

The system eventually reduced the annual river of water from Lake Okeechobee through the Everglades to only a part of its natural flow. In effect, the control measures created man-made droughts for the Everglades. In 1966, when a real drought hit the area, the National Park Service feared that the unique environment of the Everglades might be permanently changed because most of the available water was being diverted for irrigation and water-control purposes.

The questions posed in southern Florida are critical and difficult.

Should a unique natural heritage be destroyed to satisfy a growing metropolitan area? Should cities have to slow down their rates of growth to preserve parks or wilderness areas? Should valuable farmland, some of the most valuable in the world, be sacrificed to provide water for resort and retirement communities? All three are parts of the Florida scene, and all three are valuable to our way of life. All should be given fair shares of the water. But on what basis can the limited supplies be divided?

Studies are now in progress to learn how much water the Everglades requires and on what schedule. Equally important are studies to learn how much water is needed, and when, to farm specific crops. There seems to be no question that current irrigation practices can be improved. Current practices of waste disposal—such as dumping sewage and trash and heated water into streams and estuaries and discharging the wastes from the processing of citrus fruit into wells—will need to be regulated. Lastly, part of the increased demands of the coastal cities will have to be balanced by improved recharge practices and by reuse of reclaimed water. Water management practices in Miami and the other coastal cities will have to become as efficient as any in the country in their control of pollution, recycling of water, and sewage and waste disposal.

The water situation in southern Florida can be resolved only through management and cooperation. Enough is known today to improve existing means of using the water. Some improvements are already under way. However, not enough is known yet to solve Florida's water problems permanently.

7

What Price the Blooming Desert?

To most people in the United States, Arizona means desert. The word immediately suggests plenty of sunshine and little rain. The sun does shine in Arizona about 80 percent of all daylight hours, a phenomenal record. Clouds seldom block the sun because so little moisture moves into the region.

Bountiful sunshine in turn decreases what little water there is. The small amounts of rain and snow are quickly evaporated. In Arizona the average annual precipitation—a term that includes rain and snow—is about 12 inches, less than two-fifths of the national average. However there is enough sunshine to evaporate about 70 inches. In other words, Arizona is so sunny that it could evaporate about six times as much water as falls on the ground.

The earliest pioneers looked at the sun, the many vast flat stretches of land, and the rich soil and vowed that they would make the desert bloom. Today Arizona is one of our most rapidly growing states. It

Saguaro cactus stores water.

supports nearly 2,500,000 people. It has intensive agricultural and industrial developments, the biggest copper mining complex in North America, and some of the finest tourist attractions in the West. To provide for all these, it uses about 2¼ trillion gallons of water annually. Its streams, however, provide only about two-thirds of a trillion gallons per year. The difference is made up by pumping ground water. Fortunately Arizona has some of the best aquifers in the country.

How much water is the nearly 1 2/3 trillion gallons that is pumped each year? It is nearly 1½ cubic miles of water, or enough to supply each of Arizona's 2,500,000 people with about 2,000 gallons per day. And about this amount has been pumped to the surface each year for the last twenty-five years. Only 20 percent of the 1 2/3 trillion gallons is replenished each year; that is, 80 percent is being taken out of storage. This is water that was collected in the ground over periods of many centuries. Pumping water out of the ground in most places in Arizona is referred to as mining because the water is practically no more replaceable than the gold, copper, or coal that is taken from the ground in other parts of the state.

Although shortage of water is Arizona's principal water problem, it is not the only one. A large part of the early history of Arizona is an inventory of floods. Streams that are dry for eleven out of twelve months of the year become raging torrents after heavy storms. In flood they destroy bridges, damage buildings, wash out crops, and dump silt, sand, and gravel where they are not wanted.

Too *much* water is also a problem along the Colorado River. Arizona is unable to use all of its share of the water on floodplains along its side of the river because they are not extensive enough, and the state has not been able to bring its share of the water to where it can be used. Thus, Arizona is in the position of having not enough water where it wants it and too much water where it can't be used.

Like almost all desert areas, Arizona also has a salt-balance problem. The usual buildup of salts in irrigated soils is made worse in Arizona because much of the water, both surface and ground, already has a high content of dissolved material. One of Arizona's main rivers is called the Salt because of its flavor.

Problems of pollution are as yet largely local. However, even these are troublesome because in Arizona there are no year-round rivers

City encroaches on reclaimed land, Mesa, Arizona.

with enough flow to dilute and flush out the waste and sewage. Most waste is disposed of by dumping it in some corner where it can't be seen by (or bother) too many people. In some ways, this practice has benefits. It has been, and still is, used to build up badly eroded land. In a few places, treated sewage water is used to irrigate forage crops.

People in Arizona have always had water problems. Four thousand years ago, early man scooped out wells to reach ground water during dry spells. A thousand years ago, the Hohokam had built dikes and canals to bring water to where their crops could grow. When the Spaniards came about 400 years ago, they did the same to support their missions and haciendas. But it was not until settlers came from the eastern parts of the United States that the natural balance of water in Arizona began to be greatly affected.

Modern usage of water began in Arizona in 1864. Until the beginning of the 1900's, only surface water was used in large quantities. By the early 1900's some irrigated lands had become waterlogged, and the first large wells in Arizona were drilled to drain waterlogged areas. Farmers soon recognized that the water pumped by these drainage wells could be carried by canals to irrigate land beyond the waterlogged fields. When the demand for agricultural products skyrocketed during World War II, the irrigated areas in Arizona expanded to keep pace. Soon afterward all available surface-water supplies were being used. Since about 1945 most of the water used in the state has been pumped from the ground. By the early 1960's the water table was dropping—in some places as much as 20 feet per year—and damage from land subsidence was common in several parts of the state. It is hard to believe that people would waste water in a water-short region or that they would not use it as wisely as they knew how. In Arizona and in many other states, however, millions of gallons are wasted annually. Farmers continue irrigating much as if they were working in areas where water is plentiful. In two places in Arizona, so much surface water is applied that the land has become waterlogged. Oddly enough, the practice is legal under long standing regulations.

During the 1950's, for example, about 400,000 acre-feet of water was diverted annually from the Colorado River to irrigate about 50,000 acres along the Gila River, about 50 miles away. Most of the 50,000 acres were planted to cotton. The amount of water diverted to

72

the area was about twice as much as is used in most places in Arizona to grow similar crops. By the late 1950's, the irrigated area was water-logged. Not only that, but the build-up of salts in the soil in some places was so great that the water in the ground was almost half as salty as sea water. To keep the lands in production, it was necessary to drain them and to divert the salty water to where it would do no apparent immediate damage. Seventy wells were drilled to pump out the salty water and two, roughly 50-mile long, canals were built to carry the water out of the irrigated district.

Thus, to grow a crop that usually is in surplus supply, local forces joined with government agencies to build one canal about 50 miles long to bring more water than was necessary into the district, to drill seventy wells to pump the resulting excess salty water out of the ground, and then to build two equally long canals to carry the salty water away. The cost of the second drainage canal alone, finished in 1967, was more than $20,000,000. In effect, it was found easier to spend millions of dollars to build a complete drainage system than it was to change the regulations and practices that permitted the water-logging in the first place.

In spite of the shortage of surface water, the people of Arizona *have* made parts of the desert bloom, and they are justly proud of what they have accomplished. The 100 years of surface- and ground-water development have brought the state considerable prosperity. The questions that now face the state's water managers center on whether Arizona can supply water to continue its present pattern of development.

Where will it come from? Basically it will come in two ways—from new or unused sources and from better use of its old ones.

What are the possibilities? The source closest at hand is ground water at depths as yet untapped. However, many areas already are overpumped. Elsewhere, increased pumping will become more and more costly as water levels drop and water must be raised from ever greater depths. Area by area, the cost of pumping water eventually will become prohibitive, at least for irrigation, as it already has in a few places.

The Colorado River is also a potential supplier of more water. Arizonans have a plan, the Central Arizona Project, to bring Colorado River water to the Phoenix area. To do this, the water will have to be

A hundred inches of surface water evaporate yearly from Lake Mead behind Hoover Dam. Dams are not as efficient as we might think.

raised many hundreds of feet and be piped and channeled about 200 miles. The plan is complex, not everyone is in its favor, and so far no group has been able to raise the money to start it.

Other ways have been suggested to provide new sources of water. Most are either expensive or require a great deal more research before they can be put to general use. Desalting is one. Arizona has large supplies of salty water that could be improved by desalination. However, the several processes that have been developed so far are costly. Only users that can afford to pay a high price for their water, such as municipalities and industrial and mining companies, will be able to afford desalting in the near future. Disposal of the salt residue also poses a problem. Desalting as a means of supplying the huge quantities of cheap water needed by agriculture does not appear to be practical at this time.

The greatest losses of water in Arizona are by evaporation, either from soil and water surfaces or from vegetation. Some experiments with evaporation control suggest that losses can be lowered as much as 25 percent in small reservoirs and ponds, but only when the wind doesn't blow too hard. Reducing water losses from plant surfaces is another possibility. Plants retain only about 1 percent of the water that passes through them in the process of growth. The rest is transpired, or given off by the leaves and stems. The transpired water evaporates into the air and is lost for immediate use. If a machine operated at 1 percent efficiency, we'd junk it. We can't junk crops or forests and croplands, but it may be possible to make plants grow on less water. Not enough research has been done to know whether this is feasible.

In one experiment an attempt is being made to develop practical ways to eradicate essentially useless plants that use great amounts of water. Such plants in the seventeen western states consume about six times as much water as is used productively in Arizona. A system is needed to bring these plants under control. One way is to lower the water table to keep the roots of the plants from having water. However, the nonbeneficial plants, such as willow and salt cedar, are so vigorous that whenever the water table rises again, they come back to take over from the crops that have been planted to replace them. The problem is not simple, and an inexpensive way to hold down the growth of nonbeneficial plants is yet to be found.

Progressive infestation of salt cedar, 1932–64, along the Gila River, Arizona. This shrub robs the ground-water supply.

Many attempts are also being made to learn how to save a large part of the rainfall that is lost because it is taken in and then transpired by overly thick stands of trees in mountainous areas. Stands of pine, spruce, and fir could be thinned. Locally areas of juniper and scrub are being cleared and replaced by grass. The grass would reduce water losses because it transpires less water than trees, and it would also provide erosion protection and feed for cattle. Some estimates suggest that useful amounts of water could be salvaged in this way in Arizona. The costs, however, are high. Besides, the effects of man-made changes in a natural environment are not altogether understood. These changes may turn out to be more harmful than useful.

In recent years weather modification—"rainmaking"—has received much attention. The results of experiments in rainmaking give some reason for hope, but it may be many years before a practical degree of weather control is achieved.

The most readily available way for Arizonans to extend their water supplies is to make better use of the water they have. One potentially valuable way to do this is by artificial recharge. This is the term for various methods of salvaging water that might otherwise be lost, by

76

storing it in the ground until it is needed. Putting water into the ground for storage has many advantages. For all practical purposes, water stored this way is not lost by evaporation, as from surface reservoirs. Many schemes for artificial recharge have been tried, and a number have been successful. Some schemes proposed to use floods and excess streamflows for recharge; others proposed to use ground water that was pumped in excess of irrigation needs. None of the methods is yet perfected, and all are costly, but some are already in use, particularly in California in the West and Long Island in the East.

Another approach to water management in Arizona is to make the best economic use of the available water supply. Agriculture uses 92 percent of all water consumed in Arizona but contributes directly to only about 7 percent of the personal income in the state. The maximum value of crops grown by 1,000,000 gallons of water in Arizona ranges from about $4 to $10. The same amount of water is valued at about $15 to $1,000 when used to produce minerals, about $35 when used for municipal domestic supplies, and $100 when used to raise beef. In fact, in some places it has been shown that more money is made by using water for recreational purposes than to grow crops. A recent development in Phoenix plans to create artificial waves in a large artificial tank so that people can go surfing in the middle of the desert, and the payoff on water used this way probably is greater than if the same amount was used to grow cotton!

One field in which rapid advances are being made in water management is in industry. For example, 90 percent of the water used at some mines and mills in Arizona is treated and reused time after time. This is a splendid record and locally goes a long way toward extending use of existing supplies.

But in a sense, all the methods suggested here are stopgap measures. Current predictions are that Arizona's population will increase from the nearly 2,500,000 it has now to as many as 14,000,000 by the year 2000. Unless water is brought in from other areas, the chances are that water managers in Arizona will have to depend on about the same amounts of water as are available now. Arizona needs a comprehensive water policy that will help it get the most out of its own water and such water as may eventually be imported from other areas.

8

A River Fights Uphill

When the French explorer La Salle came down the Ohio River about 1670, the countryside was wooded. Berry bushes crowded the bottomlands, and game—particularly turkey, quail, and squirrel—was plentiful. Only bits of trash high in the trees along the banks, where it could have been brought only by floods, suggested that occasionally the river was not so placid as it seemed.

Up to the early 1800's, the riverbanks remained much as La Salle had seen them, except for clearings along the banks and occasional quays and wharves on the edges of new communities. The river itself was the highway for the region, far easier to travel than any overland trail. It was also the main source of water. Communities favorably situated for river traffic became centers of industry and grew to be cities. Eventually the Ohio Valley became one of the most productive farming and industrial areas in the United States.

78

The Ohio River today, at Pittsburgh

Barge on the Ohio River

It also became one of the most polluted. For a long time no one even thought of any means of discarding waste except to dump it into the river. So long as the amount of pollution was small, the river was able to keep itself clean, and fishing remained good. The menace that people really worried about was the flood, as unpredictable and as unpreventable as it had been before the first settlers came.

Although people feared floods, the more constant problem until the late 1800's was periods of low flow. Whenever the river level dropped low enough, barges couldn't float, and without barges, traffic in grains and manufactured goods virtually stopped. The low-flow problem remained critical until the coming of the railroads.

Even after railroads came, the river was so important as a highway that between 1910 and 1929 the federal government built forty-six locks and dams on the Ohio and ninety-two locks and ninety-one dams on its main tributaries. These dams raised the level of the river enough that boat traffic could keep moving. Some idea of the way the river needed regulating can be had from one figure. Without regulation, the difference between high- and low-water levels in some places was as much as 60 feet. This is about the height of a six-story building. With that much difference, docking facilities could be used, and could earn money, only part of the time, and that wasn't good business.

Eventually the Ohio was regulated so that river traffic could move the year around. Also, it was connected through canals to other inland waterway systems that were being developed at the same time. Today it is possible to go by water from the Ohio River to New Orleans on the Gulf of Mexico or to Chicago and then to the North Atlantic by way of the Great Lakes.

It was not until the 1930's, when the Ohio had two of the three largest floods on record within twelve months—March, 1936, and January-February, 1937—that the federal government began to develop a general plan for flood control. The 1937 flood was the worst ever experienced. More than half a million people were driven from their homes, and many places were out of communication with the outside world for a full month. Since then more than fifty flood-control dams have been built within the Ohio River drainage basin, and about half as many more have been planned. The reservoirs behind the dams have been designed to hold enough water to control the peaks of the largest known floods. Although the system of flood control along the Ohio is one of the most complete in the world, investigations are continuing with the aim of improving it. With records that go back only about 150 years, those responsible for flood control think it possible that a flood larger than any recorded may still occur. They should like to be prepared for it.

The Ohio Valley is one of the nation's busiest and most heavily populated regions. It includes 155,000 square miles in eleven states. (The total drainage basin of the Ohio River includes about 210,000 square miles in *fourteen* states, but much of the drainage basin of the Tennessee River, one of the Ohio's main tributaries, generally is not included in the Ohio Valley as the term is used for planning and

81

FLOOD DAMAGE

CONTAMINATION OF WATER BY DRAINAGE FROM MINES

Acid mine drainage moves through fractured ground around old mine shafts and strip-mined areas to join the ground water moving into the nearby stream. Sediment from the disturbed areas and spoil banks adds to the pollution.

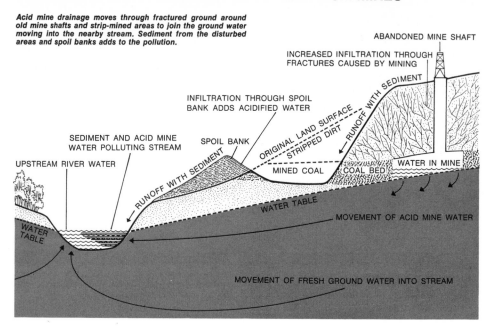

development purposes.) Twenty cities, ranging in size from Pittsburgh, Pennsylvania, with about 2,500,000 people, to Springfield, Ohio, with about 200,000, line the banks of the Ohio River and its tributaries. There are also hundreds of smaller cities, towns, and villages. In addition, nearly 800,000 farms occupy about 75,000,000 acres of land. In the upper parts of the basin, in the Appalachian Mountains, there are mines and extensive forests.

From these forests, mines, farms, towns, cities, and industries pours into the streams an ever-increasing volume of sediment and organic material, farm waste, excess pesticide and fertilizer, sewage, industrial waste, mine water, and other refuse. Also, many plants and buildings use water for cooling and air conditioning, and the heated water is poured back into the rivers. The pollution damage in the region is difficult to calculate. However, it forces many cities and industries to depend on water supplied them from great distances or to spend large sums cleaning up the supply at hand. It increases maintenance costs on boats and riverside buildings. It kills fish and wildlife, or it makes their survival difficult, and it limits the use of many actual and potential recreation areas.

Although soil erosion is not so severe as in many other basins, town developments, mining, and farming have resulted in the removal of as much as 10 inches of topsoil from areas in Kentucky and Tennessee. In parts of Ohio and Indiana, as much as half the thickness of top soil has been eroded away. Erosion problems exist also in the upper parts of the basin, largely as a result of strip mining, farming, and timber cutting. The large reservoirs behind the many dams in the Ohio Basin are still too new to be greatly affected by the silt, sand, and pollution brought into them, but serious problems may be around the corner for these reservoirs unless measures are taken to control soil erosion.

The effects of pollution on fish, wildlife, and recreation are of particular concern in an area such as the Ohio Basin because of the large numbers of people who live there. With shorter working hours, more and more people have time to enjoy the outdoors. At the same time, as population and industry expand, the areas where fish and wildlife can live, and where people can find the open spaces so important to recreation, become smaller and smaller. A tremendous start has been made toward meeting the growing demand for fishing, hunting, and recreation, but it is only the beginning of what appears to be a never-ending battle. The demand for water for recreational areas will always compete with demand for water needed for municipal and industrial development.

Sometimes solutions to problems are sought before the situation gets out of hand. As industry and population increased in the Ohio Basin, so did the amount of pollution *and* the demand for clean water. Fortunately, many people in the Ohio River Basin recognized the need for working together to reduce pollution and obtain more water at the same time. In 1948, after many delays, eight of the fourteen states of the Ohio River Basin jointly set up the Ohio River Valley Water Sanitation District and Commission (ORSANCO). Its purposes were to reduce existing pollution and to control future pollution.

In the more than twenty years it has been operating, ORSANCO has made many gains. Although its main official function is to monitor the quality of river waters, it has used this function effectively to reduce pollution. ORSANCO usually is able to identify and prove sources of pollution. It has thus been able to encourage individual

Some industrial pollutant spills, such as this one on the Kanawha River, have been eliminated.

industries and communities to improve voluntarily their use and treatment of their water supplies.

Fine as the ORSANCO record is, much more work remains to be done. Some industries are slow to comply with recently prescribed standards for water-quality control. Many continue to be careless because they know that there are not enough inspectors to catch them or not enough money to fight them through the courts.

One important source of pollution, the acid water that drains out of coal mines and abandoned coal workings, is only now beginning to be attacked vigorously. Acid mine drainage is part of a story of the industrial development of the United States in the Appalachian Mountains. In the late 1800's the nation's demand for steel increased its need for coal for the steel mills. At first most coal came from underground mines, and much of it still does. Later the coal was reached more cheaply by using heavy earth-moving equipment to strip away the ground above it.

Either way, the mines provide a tremendous new system of openings to funnel rainwater and snowmelt into the ground. As water moves through the ground, it reacts with the iron minerals associated with the coal beds and becomes a weak acid. Once it reaches the streams, the acid water drops a yellow-orange sludge of iron compounds to plaster the stream bottoms. Between its acidity and the sludge, acid mine drainage has succeeded in killing off much of the plant life and fish in some streams, made swimming impossible and boating unpleasant. In some places small streams today look like the dribble off the end of a dirty paintbrush.

Drainage continues whether the mine is operating or abandoned. When small amounts of acid water reach sizable streams, the pollution can be diluted to harmlessness. Larger amounts can be treated with antiacid materials, such as limestone— with the penalty of making the water hard. But where acid mine drainage is extensive, no treatment yet seems really successful. Some attempts have been made to keep water out of the mines or to block it from leaving them.

No one is certain today just what to do, but everyone knows the cure will be expensive. A big question is who should pay for cleaning up this form of pollution. The mining companies that mine the coal? Some of them are long out of business. Those that are still operating claim they can't afford the expense. The people who now want clean streams? They don't think it right to pay for someone else's lack of care and foresight. Questions such as these will have to be answered before the existing spillages of acid can be slowed and new occurrences prevented. The answers may be a long time coming, but in the meantime acid mine drainage continues, day in and day out.

Also, some improvements breed new sources of pollution. For example, some stretches of the river have been cleaned up enough to permit boating and other outdoor recreation. One result has been that the increased number of pleasure boats contributes a growing amount of spilled oil and gasoline, sewage, and litter to pollute the river again. Keeping a river clean is a never-ending task.

Next to pollution, the biggest water problem in the Ohio Basin is the need for increased supplies for municipal and industrial use. Even in an area as water rich as the Ohio Valley, many communities are finding that their existing water-supply facilities are inadequate for expected demands, and many new facilities are being built or planned. Fortunately, much of the basin has abundant supplies of surface and ground water. Proper management of the water resources of the basin, especially protection of the water from pollution and coordinating the use of surface- and ground-water supplies, is needed if the resource is to live up to its potential.

Many people believe that the problems facing individual communities in the Ohio Valley really are part of a single problem facing the whole valley. They think that the time has passed when local and voluntary solutions were enough. Future problems, they think, will have to be resolved on a valley-wide basis under some form of interstate or federal regulation. Eleven of the fourteen states of the basin, working with several federal agencies, have made a comprehensive survey of the Ohio River Basin as a guide to planning, development, and management of the water resources through the year 2020. Some communities still feel, however, that they should have the final say in matters pertaining to their water.

Regardless of how people in different communities and in the valley as a whole decide, ORSANCO has shown the benefits of coordinated basin-wide cooperation. It has shown also that the problem is a difficult one, and that it will take the cooperation of everyone to make the river clean enough to allow it to be used to its fullest potential—if it isn't already too late to do so.

9

The Making of a National Showpiece

The Potomac River is a national heritage. Captain John Smith described its countryside so enthusiastically in 1608 that the region became the foundation for English settlement of the east coast. He marveled at the deer, squirrels, and other animals in the woods, the duck and geese along the banks, and the abundant fish, crabs, clams and oysters. Later the Potomac became the route for exploration and development of some of the regions west of the Appalachian Mountains. During the Civil War, the river both separated and joined the North and South between Harpers Ferry and Chesapeake Bay and many battles were fought for its control.

The Potomac is the river of our nation's capital, and today some people call it a national disgrace. It has become dirty and unfit to swim and play in. The fishing and hunting are poor compared to what they once were. Both President Richard M. Nixon and former Pres-

The Potomac River flows past Washington, D.C.

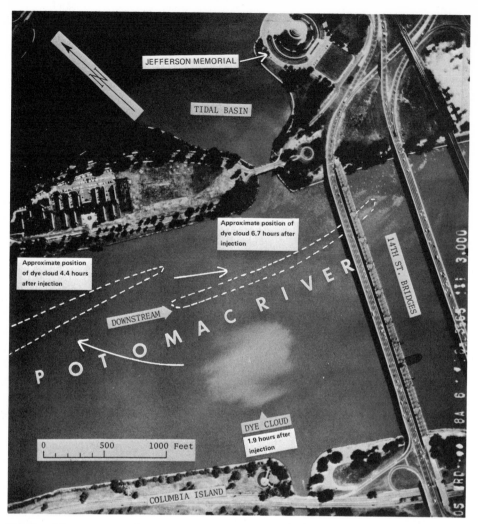

The sluggish movement of water—and pollutants—in the Potomac

ident Lyndon B. Johnson have urged that the river should serve as a model of scenic and recreational values for the entire country. Many people look forward to the day when their wish becomes a reality.

Actually the Potomac doesn't altogether deserve its poor reputation. Compared to many other streams, it is still relatively clean and productive. It is mainly the part near Washington, D.C., that is really brown, smelly, and polluted. Upstream, particularly above Great Falls, the river is generally usable and many people boat, fish, picnic, and sight-see there. True, the water can't be used for drinking without treatment, but the upper river is not as filthy as the tidal reach. Regardless, two Presidents have now asked that the whole river be cleaned up and made a national showpiece.

The Presidents' wish reflects an understanding of river problems that has become well recognized by water managers—that is, that a river must be managed as a whole. In fact, it is not enough to plan for managing the river; it is necessary to plan for managing the whole basin.

The Potomac is about 400 miles long, and its basin, four-fifths of which is above the city of Washington, consists of about 15,000 square miles. The river rises in the Appalachian Mountains of West Virginia. Tributaries come into it from Virginia, Pennsylvania, and Maryland.

The lower 108 miles of the Potomac is tidal—that is, its flow is affected by ocean tides working their way from the Atlantic through Chesapeake Bay. This is the part called the tidal reach. Salty water from the bay moves in and out of the lower part of the tidal reach twice a day, and the water in the tidal reach as far upstream as Mount Vernon is brackish. As the tides move in twice each day, the seaward flow of fresh water from the upper basin is partly blocked and slowed down. Above the tidal reach, where the water is fresh—not *clean*, just fresh—the river flows at a rate of 2 to 3 miles per hour most of the time. During very low water, it may move only about ½ mile per hour. But in the tidal reach, the average seaward velocity drops to a few hundred feet per hour.

This slow rate of movement out of the basin is one reason why the Potomac is such a disgrace where it flows past the city of Washington. The pollution and dirt it carries are just sloshed back and forth, barely moving past the cherry blossoms, the Lincoln and Jefferson memorials, and the eternal flame over President John F. Kennedy's grave. The second reason is that the cities, communities, and industries along the tidal reach keep dumping their sediment, garbage, and filth into the river.

The Potomac River Basin has no severe natural water problems. The annual rainfall ranges from about 30 inches, the national average, to about 55 inches, and it is fairly evenly distributed throughout the year. The river has never gone dry. Its natural quality is good. In the

93

Pollution corrupts view of the Washington Monument.

lower tidal reach it never was fit to drink because it is brackish, although it used to be clean enough to swim in, and at one time its fishing was famous.

However, 3,500,000 people live in the basin, and 2,500,000 of them are in the Washington metropolitan area. So problems have arisen. Small floods and minor droughts are frequent, and there is a continuing search for more water for city supplies. But the worst problem is pollution. There are three principal kinds of pollution—sewage, other man-made wastes, and sediment, which also is largely man-caused. The three can't always be separated, but they will be discussed separately because their problems are different.

Except for sediment, the main pollutants are sewage, industrial wastes, organic wastes, and excess fertilizers and pesticides from farms. The pollution in the lower basin is largely municipal sewage

94

Farmlands along the upper Potomac

and industrial waste. As in all rivers, the pollution seems worse when
the river is low. That's when the pollutants really take over. The river
stinks; fish, crabs, and oysters die; and people hold their noses and
turn away. Turning away doesn't solve the problem, but it does seem
to make the problem less obvious, and for a long time that was the
only thing people did about it.

Most of the pollution in the upper basin is local and comes from
small communities, small industries, abandoned and operating coal
mines, and the many farms. Only careful tests show that the water is
not everywhere as lovely as it looks.

The farms of the upper basin are the major contributors of organic
waste above Great Falls. This area contains four-fifths of the land of
the entire Potomac Basin but has only about one-third of the population. What it lacks in people it makes up in farms and dairies. In fact,

95

the total amount of organic waste it contributes is about the same as that of the lower basin, which has two-thirds of the population.

Although nearly 90 percent of the organic waste from the upper basin is untreated in any way, the Potomac River and its tributaries are still able to clean themselves fairly well before the water reaches Great Falls. But the water just isn't clean enough, nor is there enough of it, to dilute the added waste that comes from Washington and other downstream centers. Besides, once the water reaches the tidal zone, it moves too slowly to carry the pollution out to sea, and much of it stays in the water or settles out to the bottom of the estuary. The pollution that stays in the water is carried out into Chesapeake Bay, where it too is becoming a problem.

The organic and industrial wastes in the Potomac are bad, but the sediment is worse. Sediment helps make the water brown. It fills channels, forcing floods to rise higher. It smothers oyster beds. It makes the purifying of water in treatment plants more expensive. In fact, some people say that the only good thing it does is fill in some of the estuaries and tidal flats to make new land for new developments. And that benefit is disputed by those who wish to see the tidal wetlands maintained for their natural beauty and native animal and bird life.

The Potomac River carries about 2,500,000 tons of sediment each year. This amount is stripped from all over the basin and deposited layer by layer in the lower parts of the river and in Chesapeake Bay. The 2,500,000 tons settles out to form about 100,000,000 cubic feet, or enough to make a mud pie 20 feet high covering the open ground between the White House and the Washington Monument. Unfortunately the material being carried out of the basin is mostly topsoil, which is one of our most precious natural resources because it is the basis of our agricultural wealth.

A certain amount of sediment is eroded naturally. Farming may increase natural erosion eight to ten times. But modern practices of land clearing and road building increase natural erosion several *hundred* times. Many of the small floods in the lower basin are made worse (and the amount of dirt in the Potomac is increased greatly) by the methods used today to strip ground bare and leave it that way for months while construction continues.

Floods along the Potomac are less serious than in many parts of the

Potomac Falls at high water

Potomac Falls at low water

Sediment from municipal development mars this landscape.

country because the floodplains are narrow and the river is wide. Nonetheless, damages along some of the tributaries passing through highly developed areas are serious. Communities such as Alexandria and Fairfax are among the nation's leaders in learning how to decrease flood damage by minimizing what there is for the flood to destroy. Among other things, they seek to encourage the building of parks, recreational areas, parking lots, and other inexpensive developments on land subject to flooding instead of building high-value buildings, factories, and warehouses. In this way the dollar losses resulting from floods are greatly reduced.

Droughts, even short-term droughts, create problems because most of the water supply for Washington and other communities in the basin comes from the Potomac and its tributaries. When there is little rain, there is little water in the river, and the public and water managers become concerned over the adequacy of the existing sources of supply.

In general, the Potomac will be able to supply most needs for the near future, so far as quantity goes. However, the rate at which pollution is increasing points to the need for supplementary sources of supply. Fortunately, large parts of the basin and its adjoining areas are underlain by ground water in quantities large enough for at least short-term pumping at high rates. The ground water is largely in the limestone of the Shenandoah Valley and in the sand and gravel deposits between the foothills of the Appalachian Mountains and Chesapeake Bay. The ground water in these areas has been used only locally and sparingly, largely because surface water has always been cheap. Planners are only now beginning to consider using ground water as a major emergency source.

Since 1965 a Federal Interdepartmental Task Force on the Potomac and the Potomac River Basin Advisory Committee have cooperated to present a plan to clean up the Potomac. The two committees have made several recommendations. They have suggested, among other things, that all communities should clean up their sewage and industrial discharges. They have proposed that one small area should be made an example of how acid mine drainage can be controlled. They have recommended that long reaches of the river and its tributaries be made into recreational areas and that about forty small dams be built to provide reservoirs for boating and related outdoor activities.

The recommendations are worthwhile, but they have two shortcomings. They are not concerned with all aspects of the problems, nor do they suggest alternate solutions. They don't mention control of sediment or consider the possibility of increased use of ground water in the basin. They don't include the need for studies to learn more about what should be done, even while we're trying to do what little we know how. Moreover, they don't consider the effects of some of their recommendations on the water problems of adjoining areas, such as that of the city of Baltimore. The second shortcoming is that the report can't decide who is going to pay for the work and who will have control. In short, the recommendations are a beginning, but they do not form a plan that considers all aspects of the problems of cleaning up the Potomac.

Presidents Nixon and Johnson gave us a goal, and this was a big step forward. It is now up to the people of the basin and the nation to decide whether they want a clean Potomac badly enough to pay the cost of a well-thought-through program for making the Potomac a national showpiece.

In the meantime the Potomac sloshes back and forth, past the nation's capital, dirty, brown, and stinky.

10

The Great Lakes —
A Case for International Management

The five Great Lakes of North America form one of the largest reservoirs of fresh water on the face of the earth. All together they cover about 95,200 square miles and contain nearly 5,800 cubic miles of water. This is about one-fifth of all the fresh water in all the lakes and rivers of all the continents.

The Great Lakes are an unbelievably valuable natural resource for both the United States and Canada. They provide a waterway into and around the heartland of North America. They supply tremendous amounts of water for municipal and industrial purposes and for the generation of hydroelectric power. Their fish have long been an important source of food. They form a natural recreational area that is larger and closer to more people than any other in the world. And finally, they provide a dumping ground for much of the waste of nearly 30,000,000 people, their farms, and their industries.

Ore boat at the largest inland harbor in the United States, at Duluth, Minnesota. Since the completion of the St. Lawrence Seaway and Power Project (1959) this harbor has handled increasing amounts of foreign trade.

The boundary between the United States and Canada passes down the middle of four of the five Great Lakes. Only Lake Michigan is entirely within the United States. Superficially it would appear that problems concerning only the four other lakes are shared by the United States and Canada. But Lake Michigan cannot be considered as a strictly United States problem because it is on a level with Lake Huron. Anything that affects Lake Michigan soon affects Lake Huron, and vice versa.

The two countries have an agreement that each country can do what it wants on its side of the border, so long as it accepts the responsibility for any damages it causes on the other. The agreement, operated through the International Joint Commission, has been in effect and honored since 1914. It has an outstanding record for settling binational disputes over damages and allocations of water and for initiating joint investigations of benefit to both countries.

The Great Lakes have no significant natural water problems. There is plenty of water, the supply is reasonably steady, and the average quality is excellent—even today in spite of increasing pollution. What problems have arisen result from the uses man makes of the lakes or the uses he plans to make. The lakes are the best naturally regulated large bodies of fresh water anywhere, but the people responsible for ship traffic would like to see them even better regulated. The people owning shoreline properties and those responsible for power development and navigation would like that also, although these two groups have their own conflicts on lake-level control. The lakes are large enough to dilute great quantities of pollution, but the volume of pollution produced by the region and its concentration around cities and industrial centers are becoming more than the lakes can handle.

The amount of ship traffic on the Great Lakes, right in the middle of a continent, is difficult to believe. Oceangoing vessels come in from the Atlantic Ocean, sail up the St. Lawrence River and Seaway, and go as far west as Duluth, Minnesota. From the mouth of the St. Lawrence they can sail more than halfway to the Pacific Ocean. The main traffic, however, is not oceangoing. It is the traffic that moves between the coal and iron mines, grain depots, large cities, and industrial plants along the margins of the lakes. Navigation was and is a key to the development of the region. Every known technique is used to speed the movement of cargo and keep it moving for as many

THE WORLD'S MAJOR NATURAL RESERVOIRS

Comparison of the volume of fresh water in the world's large lakes — those containing 5 cubic miles of water or more. (Lake Tahoe, for example, on the border of California and Nevada, contains about 10 cubic miles of water. Lakes Seneca and Cayuga, in New York State, contain about 5 cubic miles, combined.)

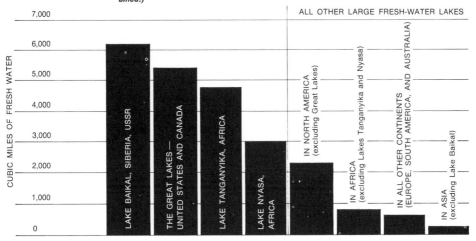

ALL OTHER LARGE FRESH-WATER LAKES

CUBIC MILES OF FRESH WATER

7,000
6,000
5,000
4,000
3,000
2,000
1,000
0

LAKE BAIKAL, SIBERIA, USSR

THE GREAT LAKES — UNITED STATES AND CANADA

LAKE TANGANYIKA, AFRICA

LAKE NYASA, AFRICA

IN NORTH AMERICA (excluding Great Lakes)

IN AFRICA (excluding Lakes Tanganyika and Nyasa)

IN ALL OTHER CONTINENTS (EUROPE, SOUTH AMERICA, AND AUSTRALIA)

IN ASIA (excluding Lake Baikal)

GREAT LAKES DRAINAGE BASIN

The Great Lakes contain about one-fifth of all the fresh water found in all the lakes and rivers of the world.

CANADA

CAN
U.S.

L. SUPERIOR

NATURAL DRAINAGE DIVIDE

SAULT STE. MARIE • CANAL

UNITED STATES

L. HURON

L. MICHIGAN

ST. LAWRENCE RIVER

CANADA
UNITED STATES

TORONTO •

L. ONTARIO

WELLAND CANAL

NIAGARA FALLS

CHICAGO •

CHICAGO SANITARY & SHIP CANAL (CONNECTS TO MISSISSIPPI RIVER SYSTEM)

L. ERIE

• CLEVELAND

months of the year as possible. But the process of helping navigation has itself created or uncovered unforeseen difficulties.

One of the earliest aids to navigation was the construction of canals and locks to bypass the rapids of the St. Marys River between lakes Superior and Huron and to bypass the Niagara Falls between lakes Erie and Ontario. Unfortunately, ships weren't the only things able to use the easier route provided by man's ingenuity. The alewife and the Atlantic sea lamprey, a fishlike animal that kills large fish by sucking their blood, also used them. The locks that raised the ships from one lake to the other also provided a way for the lamprey and the alewife to invade the upper lakes.

The sea lamprey preys on other fish, usually the largest available. By the 1950's it had destroyed the fishing industry dealing in large fish and had permanently changed the natural balance between various kinds of fish in the lakes. In an attempt to halt further destruction, selective poisons were applied periodically to the lakes in the late 1950's to kill off the sea lampreys. These poisons have almost eradicated the sea lampreys in Lake Superior, but whether the large fish can survive in the changed conditions remains to be seen.

The alewife, a small fish that feeds on fish eggs and young fish, has become the dominant fish in lakes Huron and Michigan and may be taking over Lake Superior. In an effort to supplant the alewife, fish experts introduced the coho, a Pacific salmon. The coho has adjusted itself to lake water and may keep the alewife down. It is already providing a sport and table fish to replace the lake trout, which had nearly disappeared.

So *if* the sea lamprey can be kept under control, *if* the lake trout can come back, *if* the coho adjusts, and *if* nothing else comes up the canals to disturb slowly improving conditions, then perhaps the unforeseen, unfavorable side effects of the canals and locks will have been corrected. But the correction may occur only after nearly 150 years of destruction and only after a cost of millions of dollars. The case of the sea lamprey is an excellent illustration of the dangers of tampering with natural conditions before they are thoroughly understood—of building for obvious short-term benefits without consideration for long-term and side effects.

In addition to canals and locks, navigation interests want relatively high and steady lake levels to permit ships to be fully loaded each trip and to simplify docking. Hydroelectric power interests also generally wish to have high lake levels to increase their power outputs. Those concerned with maintaining fish and wildlife want specific levels at certain times to increase fish production and protect wildlife. But owners of shoreline properties prefer intermediate levels in order to reduce or stabilize erosion along the shores, to lessen damage to waterfront structures, and to provide good access to boats and other recreational facilities. People want the lake levels regulated, but not all want regulation in the same way or at the same time.

Any degree of lake-level control is difficult and intricate because the lakes are already so well regulated naturally. The problem is to provide additional controls that will satisfy all users and still not disrupt the natural system.

The Great Lakes are so large that their natural levels depend largely on the movement of air and moisture across the lakes. More water is added to or removed from the lakes by precipitation and evaporation than comes in or leaves by rivers and streams. Yet today there are only relatively crude ways to measure the rain, snow, evaporation, and runoff, and improved control will come only as measuring devices and methods improve. New instruments now being planned to use in orbiting satellites should provide better data for future use.

Normally summer lake levels are a foot or so higher than winter levels. A drought can drop that level as much as 6 feet below normal, as it did in some places in the middle 1930's. Winds also play a major role in determining water levels. For example, wind blowing down the length of Lake Erie can pile the water at the downwind end as much as 8 feet above where it would stand on a calm day. At the upwind end, of course, the water drops correspondingly below its normal level. After the wind dies down, the water begins to slosh back and forth, as in a bathtub, gradually returning to its normal levels. At least part of the control of lake levels will have to come from a better understanding of what controls the weather over the lakes.

The vast areas of open water in the Great Lakes in turn affect the weather. Year after year, some of the heaviest snowfalls outside the high Rocky Mountains and the Sierra Nevada are along the south shores of lakes Ontario, Erie, and Michigan. Cities such as Buffalo,

WATER POLLUTION PROBLEMS
in the Cleveland, Ohio area

LAKE ERIE

boat wakes

jetty

sediment plume →

PO

I

T

I

U

T

I

T

I

I

R/C

8-12-66   4:00

I = Industrial   T = Transportation
U = Unused   PO = Post Office
R/C = Residential-Commercial

Polluted Cuyahoga River flows into Lake Erie

Chicago, Cleveland, Erie, and Rochester have to dig out from under deep snowfalls nearly every winter. These cities could save millions of dollars each year if they could find some way to predict the snowfalls more quickly or to cause the snow to fall outside their most heavily congested areas. Such benefits too can come only from a better understanding of the interrelationships of the movement of air masses over the lakes and evaporation from them.

Problems of lake-level control are today among the most serious on the lakes, but the problem of the future will be pollution. A few people believe that it may be already too late to correct the damage that has been done and is continuing at accelerating rates.

Today pollution is a serious problem on lakes Erie, Ontario, and Michigan. It is a lesser problem on Lake Huron and a problem only locally on Lake Superior. Conditions on Lake Erie are considered to be the worst, largely because it is the shallowest. Lake Erie's average depth is only 58 feet, about one-quarter as deep as the next most shallow, Lake Huron. As a result, there is less water to dilute the pollutants, less dissolved oxygen to change the pollutants into relatively innocuous substances, and less volume to hold sediment and other solid wastes that pour into the lake.

Pollution on all lakes, but most noticeably on Lake Erie, is accompanied by eutrophication. This is the aging process by which lakes gradually fill up to become first marshes and eventually meadows. It is a natural process of landfill. Plant debris and sediment accumulate until they choke a lake out of existence. It happens to all lakes sooner or later. Pollution speeds up the aging of lakes because it adds unnaturally large loads of organic and chemical materials to the water. These in turn make plants grow faster and thicker. In parts of Lake Erie, organic pollutants have speeded up the growth of algae and larger plants until the aging that might have taken a few thousand years to develop under natural conditions has taken place in about 150 years.

Along the shore of Lake Erie and up its tributary streams, the waters contain large quantities of sediment, sewage, bacteria, industrial wastes (such as iron, ammonia, and chloride salts, oil, and phenol), agricultural wastes rich in nitrogen and phosphate, and a wide variety of solid wastes from urban areas. The water is dirty, unpleasant to smell, and unhealthful, but rich in nutrients for plants.

107

Swimming and water sports are prohibited in many places. Offshore sport fishing has almost stopped because most of the game fish are gone and those that are still around don't taste right.

Out in the middle of the lake the changes are less obvious. Still, the nutrients that have found their way out into the central waters support spectacular growths, or blooms, of algae. Growing algae temporarily increase the oxygen content and remove some of the nutrients, but dying and decomposing algae deplete the oxygen supply. The nutrients and algae, along with other factors, also have raised the summer temperature of Lake Erie about 1°F per twenty years. This further depletes the amount of oxygen in the lake and reduces the degree to which the lake waters purify themselves.

One direct effect of increased pollution, combined with the entry of the sea lamprey and alewife, has been the change in the fish population. More is known about this change in Lake Erie because Lake Erie has been the source of larger commercial fish catches than any other of the Great Lakes. About 50,000,000 pounds of fish are caught each year, and have been for many years. However. pollution has changed the type of fish that is caught. Prized food fish, such as whitefish, blue pike, and sturgeon, have all but disappeared. They have been replaced by sheepshead, white bass, carp, and yellow perch, which have lower commercial values. The yearly catch remains about the same size, but its dollar value is lower because the fish now caught bring lower prices on the markets.

The need to manage the waters of the Great Lakes is obvious because of their importance as a source of water, food, power, and recreation and as a means of transportation. Proposals for management are bound to be complicated because of the nature of the lakes themselves. Measures for management are further complicated because they involve Canada and two of its provinces and the United States and eight of its states. All these have independent and differently organized institutions to care for existing and coming problems.

Fortunately, in the past few years the amount of research on lake problems has increased, and there is excellent cooperation among the government agencies, research institutions, and universities of the two countries. This attitude of cooperation has been reinforced by the success of the International Joint Commission. In addition to its other accomplishments, the commission has encouraged many efforts to

Transportation problems in winter

The quality of fish has declined.

Testing for pollution below
Niagara Falls

Effect of wave erosion on shoreline, Lake Michigan.

provide better understanding of the lakes, how they function naturally, and what may be the consequences of proposals to change them.

In a way, the nature of the Great Lakes encourages an attitude of
cooperation. The lakes are so complex that no one can be certain that
his solution, however good it may seem to be, may not have serious
unforeseen consequences. The memory of the sea lamprey haunts
every Great Lakes planner.

One of the unusual research efforts is the International Field Year
for the Great Lakes. This joint U.S.-Canadian project is part of the
International Hydrological Decade, in which more than 100 countries
are cooperating to upgrade their abilities to cope with their water
problems.

The Field Year will take place during 1972 and will be conducted
on Lake Ontario. The main objective is to study a large lake as a
whole, and the Field Year will bring together in time and place many
scientists and agency interests that might otherwise be scattered over

112

the five Great Lakes and elsewhere. Concentrating on one large lake for even so short a period as one year will provide better understanding of how the currents of a lake move and how the amount of water in the lakes and their levels are affected by rain and snow, evaporation, wind, and runoff. By taking measurements at many points within short periods of time, scientists will obtain a better idea than they've ever had before of how a large lake functions. Particularly they'll know better than they do now how much water precipitates on a large lake, and how much evaporates, and how the seasonal changes in temperature interact with other factors to determine the direction and rates of currents in the lake.

No concentrated cooperative study of this magnitude has ever been mounted on a large lake anywhere before, and it is hoped that the Field Year will become a model for future studies on other large lakes. The cooperation and support given the Field Year show that the Great Lakes region is learning that we have to know how the Great Lakes function naturally before we can manage them wisely.

11

The Future Is You

The water problems of today are only a beginning of what they will be in the future. There will be more people, and they will want better standards of living. One of the basic necessities for better standards is an adequate supply of usable water. It will be the water manager's problem to provide those supplies, but it will be the public's problem to decide what kinds of supplies it wants, what it wants them for, and how much it is willing to pay for them.

The water manager and the public really have just one problem—to decide which are the best ways to use our water for the good of most people. Many factors enter into such decisions. They include the nature of water and how it moves through our environment, the conflicting uses favored by different groups, and the many conventional beliefs and misbeliefs that people have about water. And last is how all these aspects affect one another.

Programming flow of ground water shows if supply is adequate.

There are three main facts to remember about the nature of water. The first is that there is only so much of it. We can increase the amount of fresh water by desalination. We can increase runoff somewhat by management of land and what grows on it. Someday we may be able to control the weather enough to give us more water where we need it. But for the time being we depend, and for years to come we will continue to depend, almost entirely on about the same amounts of water as we have now.

Second, water is not consumed by being used. Even the water we speak of as being consumed is not really lost. Through evaporation and runoff it rejoins the hydrological cycle which brings water back time after time. One way or another, the water we use today has been used before and for many kinds of purposes. During the millions of years of the earth since water appeared, all of the water has fallen as rain and snow, run off in rivers, seeped through the ground, and been sucked up by roots and transpired, time after time. Even since man appeared, nearly every drop of water in the oceans has fallen where man could either see it, use it, or pollute it.

One story is that each glass of water we drink contains a few molecules of the water in which Cleopatra bathed. Perhaps this is not true literally, but it gives an impression of the extent to which water is circulated and distributed through time and space.

Third, every part of the water cycle depends and influences every other part. We cannot use surface water without affecting ground water. We cannot dispel hurricanes without changing rainfall patterns somewhere. We cannot pollute lakes without speeding up their aging process, and we cannot build dams without holding back the rush of water that cleans out our rivers. Any plans for using water must consider all possible effects and consequences.

We must also learn to consider use of water in relationship to the rest of the environment. Withdrawal of ground water and irrigation have caused land to subside in many areas with damage to buildings, canals, and other structures. The weight of water in Lake Mead, the reservoir behind Hoover Dam in Arizona and Nevada, apparently has been a factor in the increase in number of small earthquakes in the adjacent region. Waste disposal in wells near Denver has been the apparent cause of some small earthquakes. Construction of the Welland Canal to bypass Niagara Falls led to a drastic change in the

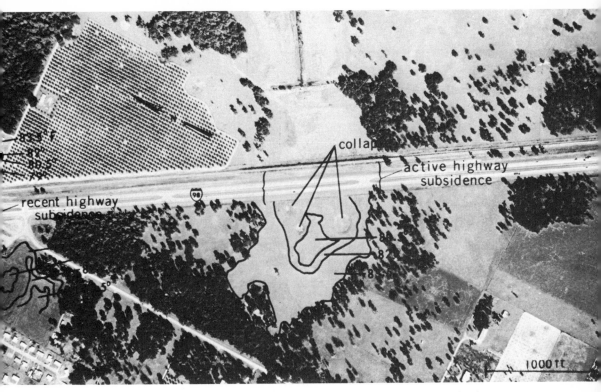

Thermal map: Infrared photography shows areas prone to subsidence.

balance of fish life in Lake Erie and the Great Lakes above it. The building of a pipeline from the oilfields in northern Alaska to year-round ports in the southern part of the state has been suspended until the effects of the heat of oil in pipelines on the permanently frozen ground of the north are better understood. The trip of the oil tanker *Manhattan* through the ice of the Northwest Passage in 1969 was an experiment to find a practical economic alternative to the pipeline to bring the oil from above the Arctic Circle.

These effects, however, are on a small scale compared to those that may result from carrying out proposals for transfer of water from one part of the continent to another. Such large-scale developments must be considered not only in terms of water needs or benefits from water uses, but also in terms of the people living in the affected areas, the animals, plants, and balance of nature involved, and the climate of the region.

117

So far, solutions to water problems have consisted mainly of regulation of flow and construction of storage and distribution systems. In one way or another, man has brought water to land that was good for agriculture or to places where people chose to live in large numbers in order to be better able to manufacture goods and to trade services.

In early times, water was regulated near the spot where it was going to be used. It had to be, because man didn't have the technical ability to do otherwise. As he learned, he went farther and farther for his water. First he brought it, like the Romans, from the nearby mountains. Then he diverted it from nearby basins. In California, for example, the water used to irrigate much of the southern part of the state comes from around Mount Shasta in the northern part, much of the city supply of Los Angeles and the cities south of it comes from east of the Sierra Nevada, and some water for irrigation in Imperial Valley and nearby areas comes from as far away as Wyoming.

Looking to the future, some engineers are talking about bringing water from Canada and Alaska and distributing it through the central parts of the United States and even as far south as Mexico. Others have suggested schemes for damming part of Hudson Bay in Canada and for creating a system of large lakes in the Amazon River Basin in central South America.

Exciting as these proposals may be, the visionaries who suggest them lose sight of the fact that we have not yet learned how to manage our water supplies on a local basis and that just because we have the engineering knowledge to build such widespread systems, we do not yet have the ecological and environmental knowledge to understand and predict undesirable side effects and long-range damages. The ever-increasing difficulties we have with floods, sediment deposition, and pollution show this beyond a doubt. At least a few people concerned with the future use of water are asking two questions: Can we afford to move water from one end of the continent to the other, disturbing the natural balance of water and living environments, before we have learned to do this safely on a small scale? And must we really divert huge amounts of water great distances, or are there other ways of satisfying our water needs?

One different way to meet water requirements has been used more and more in the past few years and will become more important in the future. That is treatment and reuse of waste waters. The idea is not new; it is the natural way because every drop of water we use has been used before, countless times. But its application to man-made situations is comparatively recent. What is suggested, in effect, is an increase in the number of times water can be used within a single passage of its natural cycle. Think back to global averages for a moment. The water on the surface is recirculated about once every twelve days. The idea is to recycle water within that twelve-day cycle, use it time after time as it moves downstream, or through a single city's distribution system, or through a single factory. Treatment and reuse are expensive, but they will become increasingly practical as techniques are perfected and as costs of other ways of obtaining water go up.

Many of the present methods suggested for decreasing pollution are based on treatment and reuse. Such practices will increase the amount of available water, but they still do not take care of the pollutants themselves. Some industries have already taken the next step, which is to use the pollutants to make some salable products. Eventually both the water and the pollutants will be treated, recirculated, and reused. It will be much like the proposed use of water on board spaceships that will go on long interplanetary journeys such as the suggested two-year space flight to Mars.

In all fairness, the future is not totally bleak. The problems of the future will be met with better techniques and more information. These in turn will lead to improved understanding and greater capability to cope with more complex problems of the future. During the past few years we have begun to apply new engineering, aviation, and space techniques to water resources problems.

The use of computers and complex models for the analysis of water problems began only in the 1950's. Although their use has increased tremendously, it is still largely in the experimental and developmental stages. The use of photographic and related remote-sensing techniques for providing data on water and other surface and near-surface resources is just beginning. Some of the methods that have proved useful to study small areas from airplanes are now being developed for use regionally and continentally from satellites. The first satellite specifically designed for a resource survey is the Earth Resource Technique Satellite. It is planned by the National Aeronautics and Space Administration (NASA) for flight in late 1971 or early

119

EROS DATA RELAY AND IMAGING SATELLITE

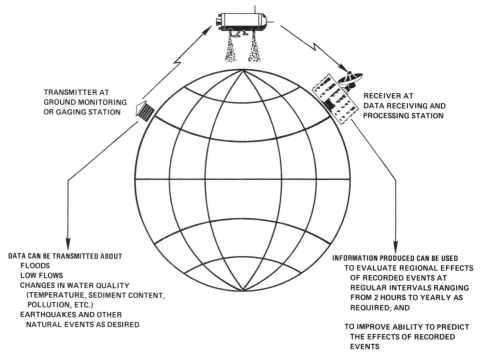

TRANSMITTER AT
GROUND MONITORING
OR GAGING STATION

RECEIVER AT
DATA RECEIVING AND
PROCESSING STATION

DATA CAN BE TRANSMITTED ABOUT
FLOODS
LOW FLOWS
CHANGES IN WATER QUALITY
(TEMPERATURE, SEDIMENT CONTENT,
POLLUTION, ETC.)
EARTHQUAKES AND OTHER
NATURAL EVENTS AS DESIRED

INFORMATION PRODUCED CAN BE USED
TO EVALUATE REGIONAL EFFECTS
OF RECORDED EVENTS AT
REGULAR INTERVALS RANGING
FROM 2 HOURS TO YEARLY AS
REQUIRED; AND

TO IMPROVE ABILITY TO PREDICT
THE EFFECTS OF RECORDED
EVENTS

Satellites can transmit hydrological information from remote areas.

1972. The satellite is designed on the basis of performance specification provided by the Earth Resources Observation Satellite—or EROS —program of the Department of the Interior. At the same time, many techniques and networks of data-collecting stations are being improved and developed to provide better information from the surface of the ground. This improved ground information is necessary to interpret correctly the information obtained from airborne and satellite-carried instruments.

But new information about our water resources helps with only part of the problem. As happened on the Green River, in Florida, in New York, as happens everywhere all the time, people want water for different and often conflicting purposes. The competition for the limited supplies is sometimes fierce, bitter, and expensive. It is difficult to compare some of the demands because there is no accepted basis for comparison. Generally we compare dollar costs with dollar benefits. This is suitable when calculating the expenses of building a dam against the probable income for the sale of the power it generates. However, how can a proper dollar value be put on the loss of a scenic canyon filled and obliterated by the reservoir behind the dam or by the use of the reservoir for sport and relaxation by fishermen, hikers, and family picnickers? What is the dollar value of the good done when people relax by a beautiful lake or thrill to a ride down the rapids of a wild river?

We have always known that there are other values besides dollar values, but only recently have we begun to explore ways in which to compare different types of values in order to make sensible long-term decisions regarding the use of our water resources.

We also have to learn that our ways and habits of living are involved. As an example, consider the many uses man makes of the floodplain. Floodplains form some of the most valuable land in the world. Water is readily available for many purposes—city and industrial supplies, farming, navigation, and waste disposal. The land is reasonably flat and forms naturally graded surfaces for railroads, highways, airports, and other means of communication. The advantages are so great that people move back to the floodplain after they have been flooded out time after time. The pressures of urban growth and development force part of a city's population to build on the bluffs above the river, but the floodplain land remains the most useful and valuable location.

Between 1900 and 1940, floods causing property damage of $50,-000,000 or more took place on the average of once every six years. Between 1940 and 1966, floods doing as much damage took place every other year, or three times as frequently. The reason is not that the floods carry increasing volumes of water, but that the dollar value of the flooded areas keeps rising as more and more commercial and industrial activity is concentrated on the floodplain.

A few decades ago people had to live, work, and build on the floodplain because of the limitations of existing technical capabilities. Today this is no longer true. People can live and business sections can operate on high ground above the floodplains. Cars, busses, rapid transit systems, and airplanes provide more flexible means of trans-

121

portation than were available in the past. Powerful diesel and electric railroad engines could connect factories above the floodplain with existing railways and river barge terminals. New and more powerful pumps permit industries to build away from the river's edge and still obtain all the water they need. There is no need any longer to concentrate expensive developments where they are subject to periodic damage from floods.

However, two things keep people on the floodplain—existing investments and habit. So long as we continue to build commercial and industrial developments on floodplains we can expect to pay for increasing losses from floods.

You have read how Arizonans pride themselves on having large lawns in a region where they are both unnatural and expensive. Such a misuse seems petty, but when it is indulged in by millions of people, the wastage adds up. On a larger scale, the practice of irrigating desert lands for agricultural purposes may also be a relic of the past in the United States. Earlier, when food had to be produced locally to supply local requirements, irrigation of desert lands was necessary. Today, with improved means of transportation and more valuable uses for the desert's resources of land and water, the need is less obvious. Almost two-fifths of the water used in the United States irrigates only 8 percent of the cropland. At the same time, more than 8 percent of the cropland in humid parts of the country is standing idle. A large part of the cost of water in the irrigated parts of the western states is paid for out of taxes paid by people in all the states. When this practice began, it was a necessary step to develop the country. Whether it is necessary to continue and expand the practice now is a question that is receiving serious attention at this time.

The day of cheap water is over. In fact, except in a few places it never really existed. People tend to overlook the long, backbreaking labor that went into building the irrigation systems that supported the successive stages of civilizations. They tend to ignore the hidden costs of modern water developments, the costs that are masked by taxes paid by every citizen. Quite possibly water management in this country will improve as the *actual* costs of water are made better known. True cost figures are difficult to uncover. They are enmeshed in several layers of taxation, in multiple bond issues, in the expenses of plants and equipment paid for at different times and in different ways, and in a wide variety of bookkeeping systems. However some rational ways to evaluate costs and benefits must be developed if the public is to be able to reach the decisions it is asked and expected to make.

As population and water requirements increase, there will be increased need for three things, and all of them are expensive. The first is more information, particularly about the effects of man's use of water on the natural and man-made environments in which man must live. The second is more well-trained people to obtain this information in the many types of private and public institutions dealing with our water resources. There is a promising and fascinating career in water work for young people with interests in science, engineering, administration, business, law, and diplomacy. In fact, there is almost no line of work that is not involved somehow in improving man's abilities to manage the water resources available to him. And third, there is the need for an informed public. It is to the long-term benefit of the public that it learn how best to meet its many requirements. One good way is to select representatives and managers who will best serve the public's water needs. However, the public can select them only if it has the information by which to judge them and their proposals.

Our water supplies are basic to our welfare. They are limited in quantity, but virtually unlimited in their capability to be used over and over again. We have only to use them wisely to use them fully. This will not be easy. Earlier civilizations have disappeared because they faltered in their understanding of how to manage their water resources. We must not permit ourselves to make the same mistake.

We have done some spectacular things in the past. We are doing them now—out in space and under the oceans. It is time we gave the same degree of interest and support to finding the best ways to manage and use our water. It's the only water we have.

Index

125

Acknowledgments

It is with pleasure and appreciation that I thank the many people who reviewed the text and offered suggestions regarding facts, concepts, and style. These friends and colleagues include S. J. Bolsenga, L. T. Crook, Morris Deutsch, B. L. Foxworthy, L. C. Halpenny, J. G. Houlsey, R. N. Kelley, Howard Klein, Mrs. J. F. Lance, T. G. McLaughlin, R. L. Nace, Deric O'Bryan, and C. J. Robinove. In particular I would like to thank that paragon of reviewers, C. L. McGuinness, who for many years has done so much to clarify our understanding of water problems through his ability to make technical reports readable and readable reports technical.

About the Author

L. A. Heindl's career has kept him in close touch with many problems involved in the management of water. After World War II he worked as a hydrologist for the U.S. Geological Survey, where he was concerned with ground-water and regional water problems. In 1966 he became the executive secretary for the U.S. National Committee for the International Hydrological Decade in Washington, D.C. One of his chief interests today is in teaching young people the seriousness of existing water problems and in helping them understand what must be done to improve the use and management of the limited supply of fresh water at our disposal.

About the Consultant

Dr. Matthew Brennan is well known in the field of conservation—there is even a mountain in Antarctica named after him. A graduate of Brown University with degrees from Columbia and MIT, he has worked on a variety of projects designed to learn more about environmental problems and to develop ways to deal with them. As a specialist for elementary science in the U.S. Office of Education Dr. Brennan sought to make information about conservation interesting and accessible to the younger reader, and he has written several valuable articles on this subject. Dr. Brennan recently became the UNESCO international director of the Venezuelan Conservation Curriculum Project at the Center for Environmental Studies at Simón Bolívar University in Caracas, Venezuela.

The New Conservation Series

America today is fighting the almost impossible task of restoring and maintaining the harmony between man and his environment. The New Conservation Series presents in an effective, lucid and logical manner the history and major issues of the new conservation. The series deals directly with man and his relationship with his environment. The battle to conserve and use our resources wisely is constant. But the conservationists seem to be winning the struggle as the issues become clearer.

MAN, EARTH AND CHANGE

The Principles and History of Conservation
by Jean Worth

THE AIR WE LIVE IN

Air Pollution: What We Must Do About It
by James Marshall

THE WATER WE LIVE BY

How to Manage It Wisely
by L.A. Heindl

OUR THREATENED WILDLIFE

An Ecological Study
by Bill Perry

THE LAND WE LIVE ON

Restoring Our Most Valuable Resource
by John Vosburgh